Joe Ambrose

PULP FACTION LTD
PO Box 12171, London N19 3HB.
Published 1998 by Pulp Books, an imprint of Pulp Faction.
Copyright © Joe Ambrose, 1998.
All rights reserved.

The moral right of Joe Ambrose to be identified as the author of
this work has been asserted in accordance with sections 77
and 78 of the Copyright Designs and Patents Act 1988.
Serious Time is a work of fiction. Any character
resemblance to people living or dead is purely coincidental.

A CIP record for this book is available from
the British Library.
ISBN 1 901072 10X

Printed and bound in Finland.

The following people have been sampled:
Dan Stuart, Bill Laswell,
Terry Wilson, Shane McGowan, Ira Cohen,
Chuck Prophet, The Heptones.

Author photo on back cover courtesy of Maki.

The following extracts appear with permission:

She sells sanctuary
(Ian Robert Astbury/William Henry Duffy)
©1986 Tayminster Ltd/Screenchoice Ltd/Chappell Music Ltd.
Warner/Chappell Music Ltd, London W6 8BS.
Lyrics printed by permission of
IMP (International Music Publications) Ltd.

For the love of Ivy
(Jeffrey Lee Pierce/Brian Tristan)
Lyrics printed courtesy of Creeping Ritual Music,
administered by Bug Music.

SERIOUS TIME

a rap diary

Joe Ambrose

Remote control

I'm in my house in Algeciras. I turn on the TV and flick with the remote control. LL Cool J is rocking the Clinton Inauguration party. It's a homey night for the President so it splits two ways. Into Aretha Franklin with her crazy Baptist dignity. Into Diana Ross with her demented street trash routine. Dylan the only white man in sight with any integrity and he's a Jew.

Last month in London a crazy black guy got on a bus I was on. I love bus travelling in the city, seeing London from the upstairs in the distance where the people can't touch me. The homey sang *Hey Big Spender* Brixton/Jamaican styley until he turned that showbiz song into a ragamuffin rant:

Soul time! Yeah, white man!

I black people.

I don't lick no white woman's cunt.

God bless you black man in your poverty to shock those awful people, that race of demons, that sceptered hellhole, into submission with your sex talk.

This is my true story. Names have been changed to protect the guilty. The innocent appear under their own names. The innocent are all dead and beyond protection.

I flick to somewhere else where Dennis Hopper is presenting Saturday Night Live and Paul Simon is the musical guest. I guess Paul Simon must be the only surfer boy in New York. He looks so weird in his wig. Simon married Edie Brickell. We were doing a show in Miami and we ended up in the lift with Edie Brickell while she was still a star. Jesse turned to her and said 'Congratulations, you're the worst fucking band in the world.'

Then I'm in the Pablo Picasso Airport in Malaga. I go to the bookshop and look at the French magazines. One cover story goes like this: *Jane Fonda—Ma Nouvelle Vie Avec Ted Turner*. The other one goes like this: *Val Kilmer L'Apres Doors*. There is a sexy intellectual looking at *Spin* magazine but she is an obvious cunt, a user. Airports are full of masterpieces of pneumatics and the lost engineer inside of me is suitably impressed by Pablo Picasso.

While I was chilling in Algeciras I watched this bootleg video of the Beastie Boys that Jesse sent me for Christmas. It was the Beasties live at Lollapalooza. In it the Beasties shout to the world: *Slow And Low That Is The Tempo!* The bootlegger is in the mosh pit so he keeps getting thrown around in the mud and his digital camcorder sways all over the place. Sometimes you get these real cool shots of Mike D because our digital hero is in the thick of the action.

So the message must be: Slow, low, must be our tempo.

Then I'm on the plane. The American bitch in the row behind me is telling her asshole boyfriend that she used to rock out to the Cats soundtrack during her ceramics classes. A South African black I saw on CNN in Algeciras said 'Sometimes I wish I was a dog owned by a white man. Then I would have more room to move about.' I went to a race meeting and one horse was called Rust Never Sleeps. I saw so much Pearl Jam on MTV. Somebody said 'There's a lot of satisfaction in a little bit of pain.' Who was it? Where am I? We are floating in the air.

I caught LL on the MTV Unplugged thing he did, doing his acoustic thing with a bunch of white boys who looked as if they came right out of the Doobie Brothers in 1976. LL had this collegiate guitarist with glasses. Don't call it a comeback. I've already come.

On CNN the CIA guy was saying that the planet Earth has been the subject of deep research from benign extraterrestrials. Another guy on the same show said you could clearly see a human face on Sidonia, which is a place on Mars.

Flying towards Berlin just as the dawn comes up, I see the cities reduced to great orange shades in the distance. Fistfuls of humanity fighting the indifference while we poor sinners float overhead, able to afford it. I look at the business document I was given by faggots in Spain. They were particularly bad faggots—so evil they'd even do business with heterosexuals.

If American faggots get to suck the military cock then, surely, like Michael Jackson says in the great world song, we should all make the world a better place for me and you and the entire human race.

Love your rocks rocks rocks. They make me hot hot hot.

Jungulism

I woke from a big nightmare one night in Algeciras on a hot sunny morning in the middle of a foggy notion, in the middle of my life at the end of the century.

I lay there for an hour listening to somebody else's radio next door, thinking about dying—not thinking that I was about to die or horrified by the dire inevitability of it all. I was just thinking about it from a point of view of genuine abstraction and laughing at certain aspects of the process that are personal to me because of being near Nigel, who lived life hilariously only to die/disappear swiftly and tragically as if a tacky magic trick he was attempting went woefully wrong.

If Nigel was here today he'd like it so much better. He'd be with me in the mosh pit at the Prodigy or Sepultura gigs. He'd be in love with all those pretty and stupid kids I screw with. He'd be walking tall, walking straight, looking the world right in the eye.

My waking thoughts moved on from Nigel to the too-real world. The noise of the radio seemed to give way to the wild wailing of Moroccan folk music from across the Straits of Gibraltar but in fact I was hearing police sirens somewhere in the distance where the Pigs were rounding up the Anarchist kids. Then I heard my neighbour's radio again and was thinking about somebody pretty I knew back in Brixton ten years ago. I drifted back into semi-sleep, my body naked and tight, half-stoned from the night before. Next thing I knew the Spanish radio was playing the rebel country singer Johnny Cash and I sat up in bed amazed to hear such music on such airwaves. When I was totally awake I realised I was really listening to Whitney (AKA Whitey) Houston, the girl who tried to kill off soul music.

The day I quit Brixton for good I saw this graffiti sprayed on the wall of a high-rise: GO RAGGA!! KILL NAZIS!! The message was signed JUNGULISM.

We'll all be swept away by Jungulism some day.

The factory

The ghost of Jeffrey Lee.
Coming back to haunt me.

We got the factory by foul means. Two Brixton pals—a young Dublin couple—moved to Berlin and left behind their factory unit, built by Lambeth Council with four phonelines, a separate fax line with a fax machine, and enough floor space to house a medium sized manufacturing unit. Our pals—Lisa and Jah Screw—had been in the t-shirt business in Brixton. Lambeth and the banks had financed them to the hilt and they got themselves a state of the art carousel that printed up to fifteen t-shirts in the blinking of an eye.

Jah Screw was a brilliant designer schooled in the *NME* aesthetic of the late Seventies. His imagery was fantasy American and macho: Superman, rockabillies, motorbikes, beers, movies, comics, science fiction, chicks, beefcake. I still wear his old t-shirts but these days I'm less attracted to advertising other people's messages. Lisa and Screw were together forever and she was a five foot nothing hard little nut whose folks were all in the rag trade in Dublin. He smoked dope and dreamed dreams, she smoked dope and schemed schemes. They did a lot of bootlegs for their street stalls in Camden and Kensington markets; shoddy fake Nike, Converse and Umbro. Screw got in on the ground floor of the dance revolution, manufacturing all the Soul II Soul merchandise sold by the ton while that band were making big money. He had a stall in Kensington Market and Robert Plant bought one of Screw's vintage motorbike shirts there; Plant wore it one time on Unplugged or something.

Lisa lives in San Francisco these days, still in the rag

trade, still fresh. She has custody of their little kid. Screw came back into my life again when we were older and less connected, so just chill until the next episode. His decision to move to Berlin with Lisa was informed by three weeks in September when they did their books and reckoned they were about to go broke. Nailed by overdrafts and splayed by non-payments, they set about dismantling their enterprise. The factory was a rental, the equipment was all leased, the phone bills were due and they got their t-shirt blanks on credit. They had a unique opportunity to disappear.

Towards the end they ordered up ten thousand blank t-shirts, printed all sorts of designs on the blanks, flooded the Christmas market, grabbed credit wherever it was going, and sailed away on Lufthansa in the first weeks of the New Year with bags full of money. They tried to sell the carousel to Soul II Soul: 'Oh, man, if you had this carousel you could do up your own merchandise, open your own shop in Camden, and cut out the middleman.'

But Soul II Soul had already made plans for Nubian gain. The whole Eighties shithouse was about to blow and there were dodgy carousels going cheap all over the world. I was in the factory the day Jah Screw finally dumped his equipment on a Paki entrepreneur from Birmingham. The Paki knew it was a dodgy lease job, gave them £1,000 for it, and Screw smiled to me: 'Kim, it's all fucking profit. Nobody wants this shit anymore and I can't take it with me. Those days are gone forever.'

Which they were.

Jesse and me inherited two thousand t-shirts, a lot of them Nike and Reebox bootlegs, a lifetime supply of cultural detritus, three clapped out ghetto blasters, lots of messages on the answering machine from bewildered former friends of Screw's. We used the office facilities upstairs but sometimes bands, including the Kids, would rehearse downstairs. About once a month we did a rave there, and sometimes I hired it to Rodrigo Gomez, who'd do punk allnighters.

I calmly renegotiated the factory phonelines with Telecom, telling them that we were new tenants. I organised it so that I burned down one phoneline at a time; for three months all business, including faxing, got done on 677 1234. When that one died from exhaustion I'd move on to 677 4321. And on and on. That way they didn't all get disconnected the one time.

The factory was situated right along the Front Line, in a purpose built development—the Angela Davis Industrial Estate—paid for by the government as part of their efforts to clean up Brixton (surely a contradiction in terms). They wanted to bring jobs to Brixton and drive out the crack dealers.

Dominating the landscape was the infamous Barrier Block, a colossal curved social housing apartment block.

Even the homeless people on Lambeth's waiting list refused to move in. Only the lowest kind of junkie scum squatters wanted to live at the Barrier Block, a mildewed cesspit patrolled by gangs of moronic black youths and their mortal enemies—moronic white youths. It got built on a curve because a motorway was supposed to be built alongside it, and it was designed to act as a sound barrier protecting citizens living the other side of it. The motorway never got built—they ran out of funds.

I did all my business in the factory late at night. I slept all day, stayed awake all night, did most of my calls to North American time zones. I started work at 10.30 after a hearty dinner. LX would drive me down to the factory; a blonde Anglo slave washed up on my shores for my comfort.

Behind Angela Davis was the off license which acted as the headquarters, on the Front Line, to the Brixton crack dealers.

Trying to drive through those boys was like trying to drive through hordes of insistent—but humorous—beggars in the streets of Tangiers. Pimps and Yardies and Yardie Bitches and Jamaican Old Guys and miserable stunted looking dudes in hand-me-downs. Those were nighttown people, my people, all trying to make eye contact with me. It was funny and frightening.

Getting into Angela Davis outside of office hours entailed a complicated entry-system involving three keys and a numerical code I had to punch into a keyboard alongside the gate. Once inside the factory yard there was a weird sense of isolation, a sense that the forces of darkness were about to pounce on me. I always proceeded hastily, unlocking the factory door and escaping inside.

First item on my agenda every night was putting on a pot of coffee. While that was brewing I'd turn on the industrial-scale heating system, designed to keep twenty humans warm in the wintertime. I'd settle down to phonecalling for an hour or two. Sometimes Rodrigo Gomez would join me there to call his pals in LA, and to do his own business. Alternatively he'd just keep me company or wander around daydreaming.

Jeffrey Lee might phone in the middle of the night when he was feeling low. He was American, kept American hours although he lived in Shepherds Bush. Sometimes he'd come down to the factory to use the free phone to ring his old pals in New York or LA. His star had faded since the days when he hung out with Blondie and William Burroughs but he was still a somebody in our culture. Jeffrey Lee was planning a 2CD Gun Club retrospective, *In Exile*, on LA's Triple X label. 'The label that broke Guns and Roses,' he would boast.

About five in the morning, exhausted from fraud, deceit and conspiracy, I'd quit. I'd ring my girlfriend in New York, do some last minute paperwork before quitting Angela Davis, walking up the Front Line, up Electric Avenue, to a spot near the Ritzy Cinema where I'd catch the first 2A bus of the day. Along the way I'd drop into the newsagent to pick up a paper and into a bakery for fresh bread.

The social aspect of it all was limited. If you're out and about at that time of the day you're involved in a conspiracy of sorts and encounters with other people have a certain intimacy about them. Sometimes I'd meet a rabid Rasta or two going about their personal business. Once I met a blonde squatter boy, aged about sixteen, and we got real friendly for a few moments. He seemed lonely, lost, tender, didn't have a name. I think he wanted to talk but London is not much of a place for talking or friendship and, anyway, it was after 5AM.

The same three poor people always got on the bus the same time as me. A sprightly middle-aged black English man who whistled Frank Sinatra songs and two old women from the Caribbean. Sad old ladies, forced out to work at that hour of the morning at the end of their lives.

The 2A would crawl through sleeping Brixton. The Fridge, site of many a pivotal hip hop, rap, or rip off event, would be untypically silent and empty.

Mr Patel would be busy taking in newspapers and deliveries of bread for the day ahead. Eventually the bus would drop me near my front door.

I'd take the escalator to our floor, the sixth floor, which offered an awesome vision of South London at dawn. I'd lean over the crumbling redbrick landing, breathing deeply of the sixth floor air, watching the big cars making their way from the distant South London suburbs into the centre. I'd see blue police lights flashing in the distance.

I'd hear Bunk, the upstairs crack dealer, fuck his girlfriend Carrie for a few minutes. Stoned, I'd whisper to myself *I am the cosmos*. Snapping out of it, I'd find my key, unlock my door, and walk into an atmosphere of rock music and ganja smoke.

Jesse would be sprawled in front of the TV, catching the breakfast shows, instant news about new initiatives Thatcher was announcing that day, news about traffic across town. Jesse and me would bullshit awhile, brothers to each other, and then I'd go to my bedroom where I'd read a New Wave detective novel before slumping into sleep. Eventually a few solid citizens would get up and go to work. But it was Brixton and most of the important work of the day had already been done under the cover of darkness.

I ain't no joke

Me and Philippe are out of our minds on scag and it's a wild teen party scene.

We stumbled through a hole in a wall an hour ago and we are in the old x-ray unit of the hospital. Philippe is just mumbling bullshit in French and I can't even mumble. Scag is such a quick drug and it makes him and me look like such cool brothers.

I've had more fun with Philippe in the last month—since he came to live in Brixton—than I've had with my girlfriend or Jesse in the last year. I said to Jesse: 'I thought all those fucking French were so uptight and anally retentive and he is not like that at all,' and Jesse replied: 'Why is it that when we have these conversations we're always having them about you and your friends or you and your lovers or you and your family?' Handsome Jesse paused, looked at the yellowing ceiling, smiled: 'Philippe is cool, OK, Kim, just I wish he was my friend too and not just your friend alone. Why do you have all the cool friends?'

And I can't say it but there is some truth in his feeling—which is that the reason I have all the cool friends is because he is the better looking of the two of us and I'm the one who makes himself available. But I can't really talk to Jesse about stuff like that—it drives him crazy.

I was still asleep in the squat when Philippe phoned

me earlier in the evening and said: 'Hey, Kim, come on over you stupid fucker, I've got the word on this party in Hackney that we must go to. Toshiba is coming too.'

Philippe has a foxy sister, Toshiba. There is something strange about their friendship. Maybe Daddy used to watch them doing it doggy style when they were younger.

Daddy lives in a villa close to the Italian border, his money made from the family connection with Goodyear Tyres and his role as a designer for the American space programme in the Sixties. Philippe looks like the idealised English public schoolboy—stern but fair—so his trashy style comes as a bit of a shock. Toshiba has three tattoos: a heart tattoo just to the right of her triangle of punkish trimmed pubic hair, an Asterix cartoon on her right arm, and another heart, this one wrapped in a vine of barbed wire, maybe six inches over her right nipple.

'It's that Jewish blood my father refuses to discuss,' Philippe tells me in the chilly bowels of the x-ray room, shaking a little plastic bag full of brown sugar in front of my blue eyes. 'My daddy is just a big fascist pig. He thinks the whole world is Communist, me in particular. And love is strange.'

'I'll take you for a walk across hell on a spiderweb,' I say, eyeing the baggie.

'Huh?' His English is good, but he can't catch that one.

'Nothin'.'

We go to a side room where the walls are turning to rubble and there's an orgy in progress. A dreadlocked man in his forties is sodomising a girl in her mid-teens. Two punk boys have their ragged combat trousers down around their ankles and are french kissing and giving each other handjobs. One of them I've seen before, from East Berlin—his pal is English. Philippe points out the beautiful Toshiba who is giving a blowjob to her usual boyfriend.

All the action is making Philippe horny and I can't pretend that I'm unaffected either. But I'm not into doing it in public so I go sit on the ground in the corner and watch. The ground is damp and cold but the scenery is picturesque. Philippe is stern but fair so he doesn't have any trouble finding a woman. And I just watch. And who is watching the watcher?

When he finishes he zips himself up and comes to join me, sweaty and exhausted. I roll the joints, he talks, we stay there until the dawn. Eventually we get a taxi back to my place and snort the scag off the green paisley patterned Formica kitchen table. When we're both in the mood for nodding off, I french kiss him and he very quickly gives me my handjob.

Spent animals, we sleep on my double mattress. Every dog has his day and every cat his night.

Serious time on the frontline/ the guns of Brixton

The map is moving 'cause it's written in smoke.

I don't know where Brixton begins or Brixton ends. I heard of it in the Clash song *Guns of Brixton*.

I thought of it as a black ghetto where the black life was lived. The first time I saw Brixton was when the band were doing a session for the BBC. We stayed in squats and I got struck the way you're struck when you first see a great painting. Brixton is all colour and humanity.

I took the plane to London, travelling alone, got onto the tube system at Kings Cross St Pancras. The Victoria Line took me directly to Brixton where I found myself surrounded by old black women with big tits and wide hips who were a vision of the black nation, Johnny Too Bads and corner boys from streetcorner society smoking Silk Cut, police paranoia, militant black magazines on sale, Nation of Islam guys trying to be friendly or unfriendly (I never could tell), fag couples with shopping bags, advertising types living locally, the sound of Boom Boom Batty Boy ragga or reggae music blasting out of record shops.

For the first time since childhood I knew that I was home.

On Saturdays all the fat old Caribbean ladies would come down from the housing estates like Tulse Hill (where the white homeowners bring their dogs to take a shit) to pick up weekly supplies. They'd trundle around with huge shopping trolleys, picking up plantains, potatoes, fruit and meat. The air would be rich with the smell of cooking food, the fertile smell of slightly rotting vegetables, the sweet temptations of over-ripe mangoes. The Islamic butchers shops with the collection boxes for Islamic charities sold mountains of cheap cuts by the big weight.

When the old black ladies got tired they'd stand perfectly still, drop their bags, rub their backs, and sigh: 'Oh my goodness!' or 'Dear oh dear!' Those were good Christian women resigned to living in a sleazy white world disinterested in them. Their conversation would be by turns spiritual or bawdy.

Brixton is life, death, music, drugs, prayer, hip hop, lesbians, laughter, food, screwing, ragga, drink, cars, gossip, cunt police, booming systems, traffic jams, gunshots, political meetings, pimps, riots, murder, poverty, perverts, nationalistic white trash, squatters, McDonalds, reggae, lonely planet boys, sex beds, stabbings, rice and peas, faggots, fate.

If you get off at the tube and you want to see my Brixton turn left and walk south. Walk on by the cheap shoe shops and the Iceland supermarket, take that first left and you're in Brixton Market, checking out the meat and the fruit.

I went down the market every Saturday.

My first stop was the deleted soul stall. A strange middle-aged Bluebeat black guy and a typical white East End market trader stood there selling deleted Rick James albums and late-period Temptations stuff. Right behind the vinyl stall was the Chinese foodmarket where I'd buy peppercorns and bay leaves cheap. The front of the Chinese place was sublet to a Jamaican butcher. On his glass refrigerated shelves he kept huge wobbling chunks of dark red beef meat. These he cut crudely, with a knife like a machete, as each customer demanded. One time this old black woman was howling at him because he was trying to sell her too much meat, about eight pounds.

'Way way too much meat darling!' she said, laughing and shaking and smiling. 'That meat is too big!'

'Not half big enough, my dear,' said the meatman.

After the foodstore I'd go on down through a market full of near-Oriental delights, ignoring the preachers, the he-males, the pimps, the she-males, the pickpockets. The other squatters would be out and about, the only white people really living the life of the market. They'd buy vegetables to conform with their vegetarian principles and their restricted budgets. Morons but I loved them.

Some of them knew me, some of them knew who I was, some of them pretended not to notice me. It wasn't like I had anything in common with them other than my desire for free homes, free phones, free electricity. They had strange ideas and lifestyles that I found attractive but out of sync with my own belief that the most important thing in the world right then was the individual possessed of intelligence, judgement, belief, hope and imagination.

For all my hesitations about those kids, they had a philosophy I found hard to argue with, and inadequacies that I wanted to take advantage of. They were the last defenders, in Thatcher's England, of ideals I'd liked as an idiot kid. They were on the streets and at the barricades, anarchist desperadoes, the beautiful dreadlocked patchouli-oiled screwable unwashed of my earliest sexual fantasies.

Sometimes I think that I was in on the beginning of something. Sometimes I think that I was in on the end.

It began with a funeral

Jesse and me had a band going together, Subliminal Kids.

Jesse was the lead singer/bass player and I was the manager, but it would be fair to say that I got more engaged by the band than most managers get. What was I trying to say with my unnatural input?

The best Christmas records are by Frank Sinatra, Nat King Cole, Tony Bennett, all those slick Old Guy crooners from America. Chestnuts roasting by the fire and Santa Claus is coming to town. Those guys had their shit together. They recorded their Christmas songs in June and July, under the hot California sun. The Nelson Riddle string arrangements conjured up the snow, the reindeers and mistletoe in an urbane style, while the besuited and besotted singers got blowjobs in the shade.

If you want a hit Christmas record, you do your recordings in the summer and allow the wheels of industry to do *their* work in the autumn. Jesse and me were always making our Christmas records in late November.

In 1986 Jesse suggested that I hang on in Dublin until he found us a London place. His girlfriend lived in Brixton, a smart girl from Belfast doing postgraduate work at the School of Oriental and African Studies. He arranged to go crash with her while he searched for a squat. The whole of Dublin was abandoning the city just then, as tales of beatnik glory in the squats of London washed up on our provincial shores on a daily basis. My generation had been living good in Dublin, making Super 8 movies and organising warehouse parties, but we were all too poor then. Dublin was a penniless backwater. And the future? There was no future.

From the Oriental and African student's flat Jesse learned the ropes. He sussed out the huge redbrick Tulse

Hill Estate which, by general squatter consensus, was unsuitable for us underground folks. The flats were filthy, the natives were hostile and Lambeth Council, who owned all the civic housing in Brixton, were kicking squatters out of there by the newtime.

Jesse reckoned otherwise, and he worked very hard to find us a home. He broke into nine different apartments before settling on the right one for us. Jesse was the prettiest star on the Dublin band scene: the girls wet themselves for him, the guys were jealous of his Henry Fonda swagger, and he was rueful, dark and burning in his ardour for music. Dublin audiences think they're at the circus, they liked to watch Jesse swallow his sword for the delight of the crowd. His passion is still his downfall on occasion. In 1986 we were all more interested in music than we were in sex.

The procedures involved in squatting, under the laws in effect in England, were carved in stone:

—Walk all over Tulse Hill Estate (piss poor protoplasm and black folks to the fore) looking for empty properties, which are easy to spot. Unwashed curtains unmoved from one end of the week to the next indicate to the jackal that nobody lives in the apartment anymore. No houselights or TV switched on or off in the evenings confirm your suspicions.

—Connect a sliver of sellotape to the very bottom of the door and to the doorframe. Monitor the tape a few days. If the tape gets disconnected or disappears then you've made a mistake; the solid citizen is at home and living life. If the tape stays in place, then you're probably right about the curtains and the lights. You've got to buy strong tape or gaffer tape to get this right. The air and the dampness disconnect the cheap stuff you get in the budget shops.

—You're doing all this stuff, watching places you want to squat, and if you're an acknowledged master of squatting, other squatter assholes will be watching you. In real estate terms, they'll gazump you. Predator squatters will let you do all the work—wandering about in the darkness looking for lightbulbs and bits of sticky tape, looking for patterns in the randomness—and then, while you're sleeping, they'll break into the place you've got your eye on and grab it for themselves. We had problems that way from a lot of Italian junkies.

—You don't break the law until you do the next thing. In the middle of the night, not so late that the poor people are already getting up for work, you kick in the front door or you smash a window; you break and enter. Sometimes you find a small window open or sneak in through the skylight over the front door. Once Jesse broke into a place at 4AM to find a terrified old woman standing in the hall in her dressing gown. Another time he found a corpse in the bed in a bedroom.

—Once inside you've got to change the front door

lock. This is the law—once you've changed the lock the place is really yours and they've got to get a court order to get you out. As with the sellotape, you've got to spend a little money on your lock, a good Chubb preferably.

—Essentially, if all goes well, when you've been through these procedures, you've got yourself a home. You put a notice in the window saying something inane-but-legal like: *This is my home. I am living here. Nobody has the right to enter my home. I will send for the police if anybody attempts to enter.* And on and on. You sit tight. If the council don't send thugs to illegally fuck you out onto the street (unlikely) or if the legitimate tenants don't return from their cheap holidays, you're a real squatter, a child of the universe with a right to be free.

—Sometimes when you get inside you find the place in a fearful mess; stale sperm-filled rubbers in the sink, shit in the hallway, smells of piss and old age. Once I found a beautiful black couple, about thirteen years old, doing it doggy style in the bath. There were three minutes of blissful voyeurism for me before they, compromised by their position, realised that I was standing right behind them watching the cheeks of his arse going boom, boom, boom, clenching, unclenching, clenching.

—Sometimes the neighbours, if they're white trash, will hear you break in and call the cops. The Pigs don't really give a shit about squatters; they drive up to the estate just in case it's a real robbery. When they ascertain that you're just a squatter they give you a caution and tell you to fuck off.

—You soon come to terms with the fact that you're behaving like an animal. This never leaves you. All your subsequent life a little part of the cold asshole lurks inside you and deals with the common people from a certain ruthless, radicalised perspective. You've seen the people at their worst, you've fought your first street battle against the State. You know what Karl Marx meant when he talked about the lumpen proletariat, the white bread TV-addicted heterotrash denizens of the underclass. You're different, you're new, you're hard.

Jesse rang me in the middle of the night from what would be our home until the Nineties: Ralston House, Tulse Hill Estate.

His message was loud and clear: 'Get over here quick, Kim. It's amazing. It needs a big cleaning but the phone is working, there's central heating, and we'll have tons of space. There are three bedrooms, a huge kitchen, a huger living room.'

I rushed into central Dublin the following morning, got a cheap Ryanair plane ticket to Luton, a train into London, a tube from St Pancras station to Brixton, and I was sitting with him in our new living room drinking tea forty-eight hours after his phonecall.

No. 36 Ralston House was spacious and dirty just like Jesse said, full of the leftovers from several layers of habitation. A straight who'd worked in computers and owned a car had been there just before us. He'd been squatting too. Before him there was a biker and there was plenty evidence of what sort he was—a slob. He'd left bits of bikes and his greasy overalls in the middle of the rubbish in the kitchen. The biker was yet another squatter. The last *real* tenant, who'd obviously hung there a long, long, time—maybe ten years—was a War Baby with a history of mental illness going back to the mid-Sixties. Maybe he was dead in a doorway or a ditch by the time we grabbed his home.

Before I went native and got into the band-managing business I'd been a historian. This education came into its own in Brixton. Sitting about at a desk over ancient documents was my idea of a good time. The legitimate tenant of our new home was important to us—it was vital that we understood what became of him because we now had the opportunity to pretend to *be* him and to hold onto his flat for a long time.

I set about looking through his files. The news from the documentation was very good—Lambeth thought the tenant was still living in Ralston House and they had him down as loco, to be treated with kid gloves. The various squatters who'd been in his place since he disappeared had paid the rent occasionally to maintain an air of normalcy. So far as Lambeth were concerned, the place was kosher.

I woke up after my first night in Ralston House, walked naked into the long dark hall, and looked out at the world through a big net-curtained window. Straight away I saw a crowd gathered on our landing. I'd never squatted before and, for a moment, I thought vigilantes had gathered to evict us. I pulled on clothes, went to the front door and opened it to see what was going on. There was a funeral right next door and six floors down I could see a hearse with two black mourning cars waiting for a coffin that, right then, was coming out of my neighbour's front door.

The pallbearers, spotty young men in cheap suits, had trouble getting the coffin through the narrow door and onto the landing. There was no weeping or wailing, just a vacant silence; it was difficult to tell the mourners from the rubberneckers.

The husband of the dead woman in the coffin stared at me resentfully as I stood there in my torn jeans and Sonic Youth t-shirt.

I was young and he was old, I had hair and he was bald, his woman was dead in poverty, my woman was a journalist in America. He lived on that terrible estate—a cheap thrill for me and a life sentence for him—with no hope of escape other than a companion coffin to the one containing his wife.

White trash gathered close to him, huddling in alcohol against the awfulness of death. In the years that followed I got to know our neighbour and we worked out a nervous *modus vivendi*. His daughter, twelve then, was screwing around and entertaining the troops by the time we quit Brixton. Maybe she missed her mother.

But it began with a funeral and the significance of that was blissfully lost on me until it ended with another one, years and adventures later.

Rock'n'roll Paddy

By the time we got somewhere, and we did get somewhere, there were no Irish musicians left in Subliminal Kids.

The band that travelled over to London with us was entirely Irish. Those Irish boys all came from the northern, unfashionable, parts of Dublin. Neither Jesse nor me came from Dublin at all, we were unreconstructed country boys who'd chosen to live in the sleek fashionable environs of south Dublin.

Our guitarist was a cold fish called Powell, a muscular blonde who looked good in jeans in photographs but who didn't play particularly good guitar. He never came to terms with his equipment. When I think of Powell I think of feedback. Not the sonic symphonies of white noise created by the Velvet Underground but the kind of sloppy noise you expect a schoolboy to make. He was a trier though, and when you knew his family you knew why he desperately wanted to be a rock'n'roll star.

Powell's mother came straight out of an indie American arthouse movie. She was in love with her microwave and believed everything she read in the instruction manual she got with the machine. She boiled eggs in it, irradiated joints of good ham in it, destroyed the finest of food that agricultural Ireland could produce. When not 'cooking' with the machine, she'd engage you in surprisingly diverse conversations about how labour-saving the microwave was. With wonderful symbolism, her atomic engine was located on top of the rings of a fine old gas cooker which was never, ever, used. One night when I called to see Powell his mother was watching The Late Late Show in the sitting room, curled up with a book called *Gourmet Microwave Cooking*.

Our drummer was Fitz, the only Subliminal Kid with a trashy background. One time when we were crashing in his home his mother went out and bought us fish and chips for breakfast. The mother was a nice old scrubber who'd been to see the Stones in Hyde Park in the Sixties while working as a chambermaid in an Earls Court hotel.

Contradictorily, Fitz's family was real rich because his father, whom I never met, was a fish fingers millionaire. Dad Fitz started out as a delivery boy but by the time we recruited his son he was the managing director of a frozen food company. The patriarch bought a different grotty north Dublin housing estate home for each of his five sons, kept the freezer in each house full of fish fingers, pizzas, quarter pounders and oven chips. This proved useful when Subliminal Kids were broke and starving.

We first became aware of Fitz while he was the drummer in a four-sexy-longhairs rock'n'roll band in the Led Zeppelin mould called The Zines. We were always predatory about good looking musicians. It was either the latent homosexual in us or else we were just trying to put together the new Rolling Stones. I never quite worked out which, but Jesse did.

Fitz worked on looking good instead of working on his drumming. He was well-built teenager in the Seventies mode with a twenty-two inch waist, a tiny tight butt and old-fashioned long black hair reaching all the way down to his ass. He had stupid resentful eyes, his balls stuck out through his sprayed-on gossamer jeans and he was chancing his arm about music and about life itself.

We recruited him in 1985, which was not the right time for his Romeo looks or gypsy attitudes. Before we nabbed him Subliminal Kids gave The Zines—Northside boys who thought they'd got lucky through connecting with us and moving into Temple Bar—support slots on our city centre gigs while conducting an almost sexual courtship, sussing Fitz out. I had the boys around to my flat for dinner, gave them dope to smoke and trendy videos with naked women in them to look at. I think they knew we were after Fitz. In a big village like Dublin we were always bumping into one another in clubs and Temple Bar coffee shops.

Fitz and Powell were the young victims we vampirically hauled over to London after us. Fitz never went back to Dublin. Powell disappeared into London, last seen (five years ago) working as a motorbike courier.

Fitz had contacts of his own—indeed a life of his own—so he settled into a huge squat in Willesden on arrival in the city.

His squat was a big deserted Victorian hospital done in the gothic style with rooms for about three hundred people. The hospital was divided into four different wings. The Australians had one wing and the Irish, South Africans and Italians had a wing each. Every Saturday night there were huge parties where Australians and Americans screwed all and sundry while crap music got played on the sound systems.

The Irish wing was full of rural Irish, and Fitz, an unreconstructed Dubliner, had nothing in common with them so he lived with the Australians. He looked just like the Aussies—styled a beach bum right out of an Australian soap opera, all bedenimed, longhaired and phallic. The only beaches he'd been on were murky mobile-home enclaves south of Dublin like Courtown Harbour and Tramore, but cold reality is irrelevant to a young man's dreams, aspirations and sartorials.

The Willesden squat harked back to a philosophy of squatting quite unlike the one we indulged in down South London way. They took their lead from the big European squats where everything was run by committee; communal party rooms raved and rocked until the break of dawn, the food was vegetarian and life was one big valley of squinting windows. There was both a progressive and reactionary aspect to that kind of squatting. Certain distinct types—experienced older men, bossy promiscuous women, militant vegetarians, neurotic blading fags, heterosexual couples—ruled the roost, and one man's unacceptable behaviour was, invariably, my idea of a good time.

It was party time for the Willesden posse. As the Eighties moved on they helped keep Durex in profit, the carpet was permanently rolled back for dancing and vast, serious, territorial wars occupied a lot of their time.

Subliminal Kids, even though we didn't know it at the time, were writing a new free market book of rules for squatting, one more in keeping with the free market philosophy of our times than the anarcho-punk doctrines of our colleagues. Keep your temporary autonomous zone, I want to be in a zone of my own.

Fitz liked to keep going until the rubber popped so I don't know why he quit Willesden or headed south. One dramatic day he showed up in Tulse Hill mumbling incoherently about needing to live in Brixton.

He had peasant cunning, if no intelligence, and maybe he felt we had superior bedfrolics in Brixton. Perhaps he knew that, career-wise, he was better off being where the action was, fending off incursions from better, prettier, or smarter drummers. Jesse was happy enough to bring him into our universe and found him a three bedroom home five minutes from our place with the same facilities—central heating, phones, beds.

This was good and bad. Fitz always had money from home and could be charming company, especially if you felt like slumming it a little. He was barely literate, the sort of lad who read everything with his tongue sticking out while his index finger ran across the line of print.

He was deeply contrived in his approach to me and Jesse, thinking of us as Higher Ups, a classy act with lots of middle class interface. He expected us to be wise, forward thinking and righteous. He thought I had great expectations of him and he tried to live up to these self-conceived standards. In fact I expected him to pass his days idyllically holing pussy, picking his nose, eating his snot, scratching his arse, eating cheeseburgers, and wearing dirty underpants. He imagined I saw him as the sort of chap who'd be reading Norman Mailer, listening to cool contemporary sounds, wearing silk shirts, cooking pasta dishes, and giving considerate New Man safe sex.

He moved two former members of The Zines into his squat. They too were refugees from the Willesden shag shack in search of a more highly evolved life-form. They too regarded us as Higher Ups—stern but fair—they too were good looking longhairs with ancient Rolling Stones albums and tight leather trousers.

It was parties and bitches and tapes of other people's record collections all the time at their dive. This was good, we got to pick up the occasional bit of stray snatch and the hidden extras that went with such girls: dinners in Chinese restaurants, the new Iggy Pop album bought for your birthday, tickets to go see Jane's Addiction in The Marquee. The deal we made with the loverboys was that we got to hold onto one of the bedrooms in their squat so we could run phone scams and frauds out of there—we held the concession on mail order and catalogue fraud. For a little weekly money we let

Rodrigo Gomez—a punk promoter who booked in a lot of the Kids' gigs—put in his own phoneline and pick up lots of computer gear on credit.

The significant thing about this little arrangement was that it gave us a key to Fitz's front door and to the plebeian sex life of him and his pals. It was cool to walk in there while they were shagging (they liked to do it doggy style on the sitting room floor, they liked us to watch, presumably imagining that because we were Higher Ups we'd know if they were doing it right), make a cup of tea in the kitchen, relax in a couch in the sitting room, egging them on, listening to *Exile on Main Street* or *Love comes in Spurts* by Richard Hell or *Raw Power*. They were typical of a generation who missed out on the dance culture revolution erupting all over them and—being musicians—disenfranchised themselves from the possibilities of chart action, MTV and the future of Western civilisation.

I'd go into the place during the daytime while the Dublin boys were out working on the building sites. (They needed a fair amount of money to keep themselves in cool threads.) I'd read letters from Ma and Da, letters from foreign girlfriends gone back home, good news reports from STD clinics.

One of the smarter lads kept a lengthy diary full of his hopes and aspirations, his sex fantasies, graphic accounts of things himself and Fitz got up to in mixed doubles with groupies. Jesse would flop elegantly in the sitting room reading out excerpts to me. Once we found this letter Fitz had been working on for about three weeks. It was to his Mammy, all about buggering this German chick he'd come across. Fitz and all around him were animals. And Mammy had been to Hyde Park to see the Rolling Stones.

We'd rob whatever washed up in that den of iniquity. They had periods of imagined stability and domesticity during which Fitz or one of the lads would keep a semi-permanent girlfriend. The girlfriends would normally last about two weeks, would be prosperous enough, and wouldn't have enough English to complain to anybody that they'd been robbed.

At the end of such relationships those girls were generally poorer but wiser. Some of them were surely in need of abortions or visits to STD clinics themselves. Fitz didn't like rubbers, he said he was in rock'n'roll and London to experience flesh on flesh. Whenever he could persuade a girl—usually a younger girl—that it was cool (pronounced *cuell* in Dublin-speak) he'd dispense with the durex.

The devil's covenant we had with him was to split everything that wasn't nailed down three ways between himself, myself and Jesse. The other boys knew nothing about this deal, so Fitz got a third of the stuff we robbed from the ex-Zines' bitches too.

We grabbed money, walkmans, cameras, sunglasses, pre-recorded tapes, leather goods. I had an arrangement with a secondhand shop on the Front Line, and the bitches' consumer durables ended up there. The German bitches and the Japanese bitches were the best for they had the best credit cards. Later, when the excellent Record and Tape Exchange in Notting Hill opened a general goods store, we flogged shit to them.

One hot July afternoon I walked into the squat to find Fitz standing naked in the hall, going through the purse of this German chick he was nailing. From where I was standing I could just see her resting pussy peering out from under the sheet in Fitz's bedroom. My eyes moved from the pussy to his glistening sticky cock and on to the purse in his hand, then back to his knob and back to her pussy again.

Fitz looked me straight in the eye and laughed drily. He took a tenner from her purse and threw the purse to me, murmuring *Your turn* gently so as not to wake the girl. I helped myself to another tenner, a membership card for the ICA and a piece of Wrigleys gum before pitching the purse back to him. He put it back where he'd found it, gave me a wink and pranced off into the bedroom, closing his door behind him. I studied the heavy scratches on his cheeks as he disappeared and I nodded approvingly.

Half an hour later, while I was on the phone in our

room, I heard Fitz bark 'Come on ya bitch!' as he wakened his Kraut beauty and fixed her with a swift anal penetration. 'Oh shit! Oh shit, you fucker!' she roared in heavily accented English before declining into German crap I didn't understand.

The asshole on the radio

The asshole on the radio is in control and in effect. First the DJ plays some hard core rave music. Then it's the qualitative research guy, an asshole who goes to the raves and writes up reports on what he sees out there in the frontline. He says on the radio that he goes into the office the morning after the rave and he files a report. What the kids do. How the kids fuck. How the kids think. What the kids use. What side they pack their cocks on. What they mean by freedom. Why they like music. What music does to them. He boasts on the radio about his unique access to that blue undersea world, home to the young/thin kids. Blonde boys with no asses, blonde girls with no tits. Lush river parade of innocence. The qualitative research dude says he has to take the CEO from Coke to a rave the following weekend. He talks about Rave Culture, the kids with their hands in the air, not listening to the music too much but living, swimming undersea.

Then they take a break from the talking to have some more music. The qualitative research man wants to hear the song that goes on about a black pearl, a precious little girl who's been in the background way too long.

A record by Sonny Charles and The Checkmates. The asshole on the radio.

Plastic little

I'd always lived alone in Dublin so living with Jesse in London was heavy going—there was a big desert inside his soul.

He'd just met this thirtyish Japanese sting who was obsessed with the dead Irish rock star Phil Lynott and his group, Thin Lizzy. Noko entertained this elaborate fantasy wherein all of the members of Thin Lizzy had had homosexual affairs with one another—a Lizzy groupie told her all about it. She produced a pornographic Japanese cartoon about Aerosmith by way of evidence. By some contradictory raw-fish-eating line of thought, she convinced herself that the Kids were the true inheritors of Lynott's substantial Thin Lizzy mantle.

Mayumi Noko, a stout designer clothes obsessive, was held together by her neuroses, her credit cards and her dual obsessions with Thin Lizzy and Subliminal Kids.

'Oh my father he is very ordinary person,' she would stutter in her bad English, 'he have small architect's firm and he own building company and warehouses. I don't know what he is doing with them.'

Papa Noko was the only architect left in Japan who could design traditional Shinto temples. Her mother was very poor too. She just owned two acres of land alongside Tokyo golf course.

Jesse saw an opportunity and he grabbed it. The Irish are a hungry race. A hundred years back we were down on all fours eating grass on the side of the road. The English did that to us. Once, a long time ago, we were the nation of saints and scholars. Yabba, yabba, yabba.

Jesse had Noko going goodtime. Their arrangement was that he'd give her English lessons, in return for which she paid him about ten times the going rate. Her English declined significantly during those years but that was a fine thing which meant I didn't have to listen to the stupid cunt so much anymore.

Japs had big trouble getting visas to stay in England and, therefore, they were always signing up to fly-by-night colleges run by shysters with bad degrees. As legally registered students they could hang in London for a year at a time, wielding their gold credit cards in Kensington Market and at the Hippodrome nightclub.

When we first met her, Noko was learning English in a dump off Tottenham Court Road.

The next year it was photography classes with some chancers in Camden. When my pal Lowry got married at Brompton Oratory he asked Noko to take the official wedding photographs. It was a big occasion—and a big mistake. Lowry's seventy-eight year old granduncle, the Archbishop of Tasmania or somewhere, flew in from the Billabong to perform the ceremony. Noko shot off about ten rolls of film and not one in-focus photograph emerged from her efforts. It was like a curse on the marriage, which ended in divorce eighteen months later.

For her third year in London Noko studied graphic design without computers at a dodgy set-up near Baker Street. And then there was a family crisis back in the Land of Yen which forced her to go back home. More about that later, so just chill until the next episode.

I was in a zone of my own—where I'd always wanted to be—isolated and happy, friendless but free. I spent most of my early months in London wandering alone through the city, changing girlfriends quicker than I was changing socks, learning about clothes and fashion via the shops and markets, excited to be checking out the new wave of heavy rock bands and the hip hop I'd first—reluctantly—come to terms with on MTV back in Ireland.

When I'd sussed out the Beasties through the video for *Fight For The Right to Party* it was like I'd entered into a new universe or, alternatively, a very old one. The Beasties represented a new way of living all wrapped up in a wise Jewish sensibility straight out of the middle ages, out of New York.

There could have been real rap in London—no obvious reason why not. There were lots of disenfranchised blacks in the city, but they were only permitted to play white music.

The older Caribbean people were funky, sound, on the ball. Their children got jobs sustaining the welfare system, the prison system, teaching—low-level maintenance of the status quo. The Lambeth Housing Department had offices on Tulse Hill Estate and most evenings at 5.30 I'd see a lot of overweight mobile-phoned black women heading for home, laden down with huge files, power dressing in imitation designer suits. They had flashy cars way beyond their earning power and they moved with a pathetically bossy self-confidence, wannabe Nina Simones. They'd convinced themselves they'd learned how to play the game. In fact the game had learned how to play them.

Fitz struck gold just when we were getting sick of his undisciplined thumping style of drumming. This French chick whose face looked like she'd scalded it in steam turned into his main squeeze and he convinced himself that he was in love. Mere and Pere were rich professional Frogs putting their baby through the Sorbonne.

During the Summer of '86 she hit London and Fitz put her through her paces. He boasted manfully that she had her own apartment in Paris, and his big peasant snout sprung to attention at the mention of such luxury, a more comfy nest than his Brixton fuck-pad. She took him off to Paris for a two week holiday.

While they were away Fitz's lifelong buddy Paul, pal of his cradle days who'd been with him since the age of five and who was the lead singer in The Zines, put everything Fitz owned (except his drum kit) into a couple of black plastic refuse sacks and flogged the lot to the Record and Tape Exchange.

When Fitz returned, all tanned and sophisticated, Paul told him that Jesse stole his shit, that he'd been seen leaving the squat with everything. Fitz instantly lost his boulevardier sophistication and recollected a few North Dublin epithets not normally heard in Parisian society. He rounded up a posse of five Dublin lads and marched over to Ralston House at six in the evening to confront us.

Jesse was away overnight and I was just up. When I answered the door I was confronted with large dollops of semi-violent recrimination, much grimacing and clenched fists akimbo. The real leader of the gang was not Fitz, an easily led dumb mutt, but his old pal Paul. I theatrically pointed out to Fitz, who by this stage was standing in my hallway, that if he had any kind of a brain in his head he'd have worked out that Paul was the guilty party: 'If you weren't so in love with that fucking worthless lazy scumbag you'd see that he's the very man who would grab every knickers you ever owned and flog it for tuppence.'

Fitz was much taken aback to hear a university educated Higher Up like myself talking in such low street tones, and his next outburst had a hilarious aspect. It emerged that he'd believed, all along, that Jesse and me were in league with the IRA. The very next thing he did was march towards me, both fists raised for fisticuffs, shouting: 'Kim, I don't give a shit about you or your fucking Provo friends. I'm going to kill you right now.'

Quick on the uptake, I withdrew from his range and went with his preconceptions.

'Let me tell you motherfucker,' I shouted, 'that if you lay one hand on me all belonging to you will be wiped out by Republican forces before the week is out.'

This did the trick superbly. There was a considered silence for a moment and the jackals retreated.

Fitz marched out the front door, shouting over his shoulder: 'I'll see the two of yez later and sort yez out for good Yez are two fucking queers.' This was the last that anybody heard about his stolen goods.

It was also, all bands depending on fraternity of some sort, his exit from the Kids. When Jesse came home two days later he laughed until the tears poured down his face. Fitz kind of kissed and made up with us before heading off to Paris where, incredibly enough, legend has it that he went to university. That old index finger must've been worn to a thread as he pored over learned textbooks, as must his knob, and infinite specimens of French pussy.

I don't even remember who replaced Fitz, I think it was an Italian millionaire's al dente son called Gio who wore a black leather jacket. But Fitz's departure marked the end of my life amongst the Irish. From then on the Kids became international like London and, for me, the real adventure of living in Brixton without tangible or sentimental connection to the Shamrock Shore began.

With Fitz out of the picture Paul got control of their squat and we plotted our revenge.

Paul, preoccupied with launching a new version of The Zines, was so stupid that he never changed his squat's door locks although our deal with Fitz ended when I threatened to hand him over to the tender mercies of the IRA. Paul installed some nightclub trash he knew in the flat—a manager at The Fridge and his porcine girlfriend who dressed in dominatrix black silks and satins. A tall thin handsome French boy—Philippe—who was obviously rich, with a real good sound system, some well stitched bespoke silk suits and a series of very thin girlfriends that he stuffed at the weekends, moved into what used to be our office.

Philippe and me saw eye to eye about everything, shared an obsession with the hip hop club scene, and for months we were big pals, luxuriating in an underground party scene where the girlies came easy and the sperm, waiting until it was good and ready, came reluctantly.

One night when Paul, Philippe and the rest of them were off in Brighton for the weekend, we emptied the entire place. Every cassette, rubber, sock and album. Having a personal interest in him, I did in Philippe's room myself while Jesse did the rest of the squat. I'd been intimate with both Philippe and his sister Toshiba, so I went through his room with a hard-on, delighted to be collecting his jeans, his underclothes, his letters from girlfriends, his personal photographs, his records. I got so hard in the end that I went into the bathroom and gave myself a handjob. The squat grew rank over the three hours that we were robbing it, the mingling smells of dust, dirty clothes, perfume and anti-perspirant rising to the surface. We stored their gear in a storage squat at the other end of Tulse Hill.

They were devastated when they got back from Brighton the next day, and life for them was never quite the same again.

I slept with Philippe the night he returned, mounting him violently and without Vaseline by way of consolation. He wanted to go back to Paris after the robbery and he'd have been absolutely right to have done so.

'London is no place for a boy like you, man,' I said to him when we were sharing a joint as the sun came up. 'They'd kill you for the fun of it in this city.'

Philippe never left London. But I did.

The unmarked black helicopter they use with the heat-sensitive cameras to detect the hydroponic gardens is flying overhead.

I know Jay has a plantation growing in a fifth floor apartment, so I watch the chopper with my vacant eyes. It's early evening and I'm smoking my first joint of the day. Hydroponics requires hothouse heat to make the grass grow big and fast. The Pigs watch out for huge electricity bills and they send out the heat-sensitive choppers to spot apartments giving off insane quantities of heat.

Jay has all his windows sealed off and insulated so the heat won't show…but you never know.

The helicopters are the most disturbing thing about living here. Any trouble with the niggers and they send in the choppers. The helicopter is a weapon of war and I'm living in the combat zone.

First time the Pigs introduced helicopters was in Berkeley California in April 1970. That April Fool's Day the mayor, called Wallace Johnson, along with his city council, told the citizens of Berkeley that they needed to have Pigs in the air. It was a beautiful sultry California day in the California sun when they all got together to rap about chopper feasibility. Sheriff Bruce Dykes told the folks that the crime rate was soaring to new heights and that this was all due to the drug problem in the campus area, where radicals like Angela Davis hung out and acted uppity. The sheriff's audience stood up and burst into applause. And, the sheriff concluded, the whole goddamn thing was due to confrontation-oriented radical politics.

The helicopter is a weapon of counter-insurgency. DaVinci designed them as machines of war. The Americans used them in Vietnam. The Pigs saw them in action in Vietnam between 1960 and 1964. By the end of that decade Pigs all over America wanted to have the fucking things. In Philadelphia, when the Pigs got their helicopters, the Police Tactical Squad got lessons on how to shoot from the air.

Back in Berkeley in 1970 there were dire warnings that the choppers would be shot down from the sky. The meeting was told that the proposed helicopters would be equipped with spotlights, sirens and loudspeakers. It was the Women's Liberation types who organised most of the opposition. The meeting ended in chaos, just like society will. A twelve year old white boy got the final word on the live broadcast of the debate on

TV station KQED.

The boy got up, the camera focused on him, and he shouted: 'Fuck the Pigs, and fuck the Establishment.'

Somebody got murdered

On a Monday in the afternoon I was walking home.

I think it was a July afternoon and I think it might have been 1987. I'd been to Brixton Market to pick up things for dinner. Courgettes and mushrooms and plantains and tomatoes and carrots and onions and stuff. Also I got some pitta bread, cheese, flour, fresh herbs, peaches, pears, cream.

We were having dinner guests but not important ones because if they'd been important I'd have bought some meat. Honoured guests got meat, necessary visitors got the vegetarian menu.

I was walking uphill away from Brixton town, heading for Tulse Hill Estate without a care in the world, when I noticed more people than usual walking fast or running towards me and gesticulating, their faces flushed or pale. I paid no mind because I'd smoked some Afghan before leaving my squat and was in well abstracted form. As I kept walking on uphill more and more people ran towards me, down the hill, away from something, some of them pointing to the building alongside which I was now walking.

'Is it serious?' said one ragamuffin to another: the two of them dressed in expensive bright red sports gear.

'Yeah, mon, I think it could be a serious thing,' said the other taller and seemingly wiser ragamuffin.

Most of the people I saw doing the walking and running were white and English, their concerns or fears not a part of my universe. But when I saw the black man take an interest in the situation, then I knew it was something of interest to me too because if it didn't matter to the blacks, surely it didn't matter to me either.

My life was like walking through a foreign city where you don't understand the language: I'd hear words and phrases, take note of gestures and body language; I might get lost or construct elaborate scenarios based on very small amounts of reality. That day I reckoned I'd worked it all out for myself. Some dude, some old dude, had had a heart attack and everybody was in a tizzy, the community was pulling together, people were ringing for ambulances and doing the right thing. I soon snapped out of that bullshit—if you get a heart attack in the streets of London they'll just as soon go through your pockets and grab what's going as call for an ambulance.

I walked off the footpath into the courtyard where all the action was happening.

A crack dealer I'd seen around was lying on the ground, all his limbs moving involuntarily while blood poured out of his neck and brain matter was splattered all over. His five year old daughter, a beautiful half-Oriental black girl in Adidas gear, was standing alongside him and three women from the building were dragging her away, distracting her, comforting her. A boy about fifteen was leaning over the dying dealer, trying to mop up some of the blood with his t-shirt, talking gently to the stricken gangster.

I walked right up to the scene. The dealer seemed sentient and aware. His eyes flashed on me, he turned away, his limbs just kept on trashing pathetically.

I could hear the ambulances and police sirens in the near distance, announcing that the State was on the way. They were in no particular hurry because, after all, this was just a black man on the ground. One less vote against Thatcher.

I walked away from the immediate area just as the first cop car pulled into the yard. While they were getting on with their paranoid assessment of the situation an old black woman told me in detail what had happened.

The dealer had been kicking a ball in the yard with his daughter and some youths when two black guys in their early twenties dressed in smart suits walked into the lot and approached him. When he saw them coming he screamed to his girl to get inside and began running away. The men made no effort to pursue him, pulled their pistols, took aim and shot him four or five times in the back while the little girl just stood there, taking it all in silently. Then they put the guns back inside their jackets and walked calmly out onto the road where a big black limousine waited for them.

They stepped into the back seat, the old lady heard ragga music blaring out of the limo, and the killers cruised away slowly but surely.

Wheels of steel

Was LX the victim or the culprit?

LX answered an ad Jesse put in the *Melody Maker* and washed up on our shores after Jesse interrogated him by phone. His father was a rightwing solicitor specialising in intellectual property. His mother came from a family of semi-professional painters. She'd studied at the Slade in the Sixties when it was the coolest and grooviest of the cool and groovy.

The LX family lived in a backwoods Cornwall village where LX and his two brothers, three tall thin blondes designed to please women, grew up disreputably. LX was the apple of his mother's eye and there was nothing that he could do to displease her. She doted on her son, a totally worthless leech and beach bum. She was one of those trendy Sixties parents who felt it was cool that her son was screwing around, cool that he was smoking the ganja, cool for him to be the guitarist in a rock'n'roll band. As far as I'm concerned those are *not* natural maternal instincts but a very specific English Protestant phenomenon.

LX had a big knob, both thick and long. He confided in me that he'd shagged twenty women, most of them much older than him, by the time he was fifteen. I don't think he was boasting because one night when Jesse told LX that I'd said he had a big knob LX got all emphatic: 'I do *not* have a big knob. It's perfectly average.' He grew up with lots of food on the table, lots of pussy lurking under every bush, dealing bad drugs, taking bad drugs, happy to let his cock protrude through skin tight jeans, happy to meet and sorry to part. An idealised post-punk Shropshire Lad listening to Bob Dylan and searching for love in a loveless land. No wonder LX got married when he was seventeen.

The country boy got addicted to speed, and fell in with phenomenally lowlife itinerant gypsies living in a trailer park five miles out of town. One of the trailer trash was a forty-eight year old divorcee with three sons, the eldest of whom was a fine lad of fifteen. She was a speed dealer, as were her two biker brothers, also resident in mobile homes in the same park. LX moved in with this bitch and spent about seven months in bed, nodding off on speed, sleeping, occasionally servicing the lady, never washing. Then he made his big decision and married her to get a lifetime's supply of free speed. He developed an abnormal relationship with her oldest boy, essentially his contemporary.

The matrimony years were passed by our hero flitting between his folks' house and the trailer park, soaking everybody dry while trying to stay awake. About a year into the marriage it dawned on him that there was something tragically wrong with his lifestyle but, because of his biker in-laws, he was afraid to do anything about it. Eventually, in the middle of the long winter's night of the soul, having contemplated his wife's wizened old tits under the influence of magic mushrooms, he freaked out, got out of bed and strode through the trailer park naked in the rain, crying his eyes out while moaning slowly to himself. The tears of a clown, when there's no-one around. In certain circumstances walking naked in the rain can be sensually nice, but this was not one of them. After an hour he went back into the marital home, dried himself off, got dressed, filled his backpack with food, drugs, a little money, and ran away into the night.

Three days later he reached Norwich, a boring-as-shit provincial city somewhere north of London where a few of his school pals attended university. He got a crappy job in a canning factory, and replied to our *Melody Maker* ad two months into the Norwich sojourn.

Jesse auditioned him the same day he auditioned eight

other guitarists. All the others were freaks or Neanderthals or closet gayboys. LX'd posted us this demo he'd recorded back home in Cornwall before his nuptials. The best of the tunes was a folk-influenced instrumental making a lot of internal sense, arguing a case and winning the argument. Two telephone conversations later he presented himself at our dank rehearsal studio under railway arches near Elephant & Castle.

I liked the fact that he was patently poor and lonely, that he was cold and thin. His guitar playing was as uncouth and ropy as his appearance but I was no Adonis myself so that wasn't an issue.

LX had a crude magnetism, pale green skin, long dyed blonde hair and enough adolescent arrogance to get by. Maybe it's because he looked good that we wanted him in the Kids; I certainly admired his playing a lot more than Jesse did. I was in love with the school of fucked up guitarists. LX took his name from that most fucked up of all guitarists, the junkie king of Memphis, Alex 'LX' Chilton. The conflict between competence and inspiration is central to all 20th Century art, and I vote for inspiration every time. Watching LX playing his guitar, which I did a lot in rehearsal rooms, on stage and in his bedroom, was like watching the most beautiful and innocent country girl frigging herself gently, slowly, all day and all night.

LX remained in our lives for three years, longer than

any other musician. During these years he grew close—separately—to both singer and manager. Jesse and he related to each other as musicians and there was always a certain crazed tension and slackness between them.

By the time the beautiful trip came to an end LX's inability to deliver the specific kind of guitar playing that Jesse wanted in his songs caused a big sour breach between them. They were like a young married couple who wanted a baby and who were screwing all the time with that in mind, only all they were achieving was orgasms and wet sheets—the babies just wouldn't come. Certainly LX was the one with the weak seed—by any technical definition his guitar playing wasn't up to scratch. Jesse knew this from day one, though, and if he'd wanted to pursue virtuosity he should have played jazz or heavy metal. Perhaps LX's playing had more in common with Jesse's own flipped-out sensibility than he was willing to admit.

For all that, there was chemistry of a sort between them. The Cornwall boy down in London with his faded clothes, his nice mind, his expensive Mum-bought guitar, his tight ass, his country style, was to Jesse's liking.

'What do you make of him?' Jesse asked me earnestly on several occasions.

'I guess I like him,' I'd always reply, 'I like having him with us.'

'Do you think he's a good guitarist?' would always be

the next question.

'I like him myself, anyway.'

'Hmm...'

He moved into the spare bedroom in our squat. He lived off us and with us for six months. We gave him better clothes and our crazy talk while he told us what England was like. I'd been to visit Manchester one long weekend but Jesse'd never been outside London, and I'd never been anyplace else.

LX explained the nation to us, how the Pigs worked, what you could get away with, what parts of the country were cool. For three years we saw him all the time, seven days a week. He'd eat with us every day, listen to my records, go with us to late night double bills at the Ritzy, allnighters at the Scala cinema near King's Cross, nightclubs and on occasional bursts of foreign travel.

LX could drive, something no other Subliminal Kid had ever been able to do up until that point. (Nigel could drive to the extent of being a professional getaway driver but he came to us later when he was both banned from and incapable of driving.)

LX's driving license made him a real asset so Jesse bought a car. Our dealer Boycott, a fortyish longhair who ran the South London Legalise Cannabis Committee, sold us our first banger, a purple unlovely Seventies Toyota with more rust than metal in its chassis. Boycott said the Toyota was only suitable for London travelling and would not survive passing the city limits. Three months later it expired in the middle of the night on a deserted motorway after a satori me and LX made to Brighton.

The following week LX got up early, bought the Monday edition of *Loot* and found the car I'd always wanted, the whiteboy's Mercedes, one of those canary yellow Volvo estates beloved of antique dealers everywhere. In that Volvo we had some fine adventures, stayed in a whorehouse in Newcastle, saw a massive satellite earth station in Cornwall, got to see the four corners of England. We only came out at night and, being creatures of the night, were totally out of step with the brash commuting establishment then in full effect.

A lot of the London car travelling involved just me and LX because Jesse was not fond of the uptown daytime world.

LX and me got together on illegal fraud scams that necessitated regular visits to convenience addresses in Elephant & Castle and Islington. Many a hot summer evening was passed in city centre traffic jams as we Robin Hoods, feared by the rich and loved by the poor, went about our serious business. We'd be sitting in a traffic jam, stoned and bullshitting, the windows down, the tape deck blasting road music.

We played elegant road music in the Volvo…Chuck Berry or The Ramones or Danzig. Rap and hip hop were not yet at the centre of the universe when LX became our slave but I do recall that he had the Beasties in his collection before he left us.

He was an eccentric driver at the best of times but I never gave a shit how long it took us to get from A to B, I was operating on the uppity scale. Those drives were my first experiences of central London. Several times we got stranded for hours in traffic jams on Shaftesbury Avenue, with LX worrying that we might run out of petrol because: 'Yes, actually, Kim, you know I didn't put that fiver you gave me for petrol into petrol? I just put in a pound's worth.'

I'd sit there happily while the streets filled and emptied of power dressed females and hormonally-challenged men, all dressed in clothes they couldn't afford heading for cars they didn't really own. They were doing their experiment in living and we were doing ours.

Kerouac and Burroughs discovered America on the road. We discovered England with LX. I miss him, Jesse misses him less.

LX beats me every time at the Michael Jackson Moonwalker video game in the last arcade on the pier.

Jesse would love it if he were here instead of being stranded in Ireland surrounded by savages. LX wants to keep playing video games a while more, he's younger, I'm only interested in Moonwalker so I leave him to it and stroll away, arranging to meet him in an hour at the groovy postcard shop on the other end of the pier.

I'm sitting on a bench watching a fifteen year old couple kissing and cuddling against the pier rails when I notice this flabby middle aged tramp circling my perimeters and I'm thinking *Oh, fuck, it's queertime, here comes the queers, here comes everyone.* Sure as night follows day he moves closer and I'm thinking of getting to fuck away because sometimes the queers are young or clean or intelligent and you've got to give them the time of day, live and let live, but this one is no oil painting unless you're thinking of Goya's black sketches of madness. Now he is right in front of me making initial small talk and I'm responding negatively, thinking about hegira. 'Do you mind if I sit with you?' he says, and something in his voice tells me that he may be queer OK but he's not chatting me up, and soon he is telling me that he has this spare bottle of methadone.

'I'm a heroin addict and they say you shouldn't mix methadone with heroin,' he says matter of factly, 'so I've got my weekend supply of methadone left over because I did heroin over the weekend.'

He waves the little brown bottle in front of me and says: 'If you had to buy this off a dealer it'd set you back forty quid but I can't touch it because I'm back on the heroin and you can't mix the two. I'm going to the clinic in the morning and they'll give me a new bottle so I don't need it anymore.'

I tell him I've taken scag once or twice, I've never injected, just sniffed, but I don't say more so he hands me the bottle to inspect it. The seal is broken, this could be a tourist scam. He isn't offering a free sample so I pass on the deal.

LX and me end up at a beach party where he gets off with a sweet black angel from Streatham while the DJ is mixing Public Enemy, Ruthless Rap Assassins and Eric B & Rakim. He is perhaps a totally righteous DJ and much of the music is immense but why is it that the music is all black and he is all white? The English have always regarded American black music and American black vitality, born out of immense exploitation and disenfranchisement, as a suitable blueprint for their corrupt hedonistic reactionary lifestyles. Look at that fuck Eric Clapton in his thief's suits, playing the blues while pronouncing that the niggers should go back where they came from.

In the middle of the night our rustbucket is two miles out of Brighton on the motorway taking us towards Brixton and we're talking about the junkie on the pier when this colossal bang, like a missile exploding, envelops us. The car grinds to a slow halt and, without bothering to look at the engine or anything, LX says: 'I think it could be curtains for the old car.' which indeed it is. He spends half an hour doing his best to get it going, peering under the boot with his flashlamp, before suggesting that he should call a man from the AA.

In his squat LX found this magic AA card which summons forth, via a freephone call, emergency services who will either get your car going or, failing that, tow you back to your home address. The rustbucket breaks down every week and has to be revived or towed home so often that last week the AA wrote a nice letter suggesting that the cardholder should consider purchasing a new car.

LX agrees that he must grab his card, disappear into the darkness and silence of the motorway and bring the AA to our rescue. He is deeply worried, familiar with the code of the road since his reckless Cornwall car-driving youth.

'Amm...these phones they have on motorways normally connect you directly to the nearest police station and I may have to go through the Pigs to get at the AA, which could cause problems since the AA card is not in my name,' he explains hesitantly, sounding all responsible and adult just like his asshole father. He is giving me fair warning that we poor sinners and lawbreakers are about to interface with the Pigs and the society they protect. He walks away.

I piss off the side of the motorway into the void down below before I go sit in the car. The occasional truck hurtles by while I listen to disgusting ballroom dancing music on the radio.

Twenty minutes later LX returns, pale faced and in trauma.

He has indeed spoken to both the Pigs and the AA, and explained to both parties that our rustbucket has expired on the motorway in the middle of nowhere in the middle of the night. LX, code of the road to the fore again, believes that we will shortly be joined by the Pigs. 'They don't really approve of cars breaking down on the motorway, it makes them suspicious,' he explains nervously, 'and the further you get from London the more paranoid they are about old bangers like this. They've probably searched for us on the security cameras since getting my call. They could be looking at us right now. It's only a matter of time before some of those assholes come out to have a sniff of us.'

He suggests that we either consume or throw away any drugs we have on us. Since we've been partying all night there's not much left to swallow. I've got an E and LX has a little grass he was given by his Streatham bitch. We divide the drugs democratically between us and eat the lot just before a police car cruises into view over the next hill, as predictable as a TV movie, proving that LX knows his stuff.

LX has a very bad effect on Pigs and these two—a yokel Brighton one pushing towards retirement and an ambitious younger one, a little terrier looking to score some points—inform him that they believe he may be carrying drugs. In the final end nothing comes of their intervention—they just pat LX down and search his pockets. Morons that they are, they cruise off into the night without asking us two punk longhairs in a seventy quid car how we come to have state of the art digital Automobile Association insurance but little evidence of any other interface with civilisation.

That inquiry comes next. The Pigs disappear over one horizon to our south and the orange flashing lights of the AA van loom up over the horizon to the north. As it grinds to a halt in front of us we are confronted by the biggest fucking pick-up truck in the world with more coloured flashing lights than a video games arcade. There is no sign of the reassuring logo of the AA anywhere on the vehicle. A six foot fortyish redneck monster climbs down from his cab, we can hear Tina Turner blasting out of his sound system—you're simply the best, better than all the rest.

LX mutters *Oh, shit, oh fuck* and I agree with him.

The driver strides towards us like Charles Bronson, clipboard in hand, eyes darting from LX to me and back again. The man already knows that this is weird, and he is right.

LX is a spineless fucker but man enough to walk forward and deal with our rescuer. I blend off into the darkness to watch what's happening. The dude explains that he is the local contractor handling emergency call-outs on behalf of the AA in the middle of the night on the weekends. He shows LX his ID and LX shows him his AA card, two tough guys exchanging credentials man-to-man. He says he needs to phone in our details to AA Central before undertaking the journey, which will cost about three hundred quid. It is obvious to this fucker that me and LX are penniless, that the car is worthless and that we're the most dubious AA customers he has ever seen. As luck would have it, LX has a tricky deceptive middle-class accent which maybe convinces Mr AA that LX is a student, that his dad has paid our insurance.

The next hour is all terror. After ten minutes of crackly talk on the cab radio the AA approves our card, so long as LX can produce his paperwork when we reach Brixton. There is no paperwork there, naturally enough, and we travel up to London in the asshole's cab, the rustbucket hitched up behind us, The Carpenters replacing Tina Turner when her tape comes to an end. By way of light conversation, while we're on top of the world looking down on creation, our host explains that he was in the SAS in Northern Ireland for six years. When I hear this I shut the fuck up so he won't catch my Irish accent.

We stop off at an all-night garage because the driver

wants to have a piss. I hurriedly explain to LX, while the bastard is in the toilet, the plan that we must follow. When we reach Tulse Hill we must give him directions to Ralston House, we must go into the block together to get the AA documentation, go to the ninth floor and hide in a place Jesse is in the process of squatting. I have the keys.

This works. He cruises into our yard at 5AM, pulls up in front of Ralston, we alight and take the lift to the fourth floor, get out and very silently climb up the stairs to the ninth floor. When we are comfortably sitting in the darkness and security of the new squat we can hear him in the courtyard way down below bellowing: 'Where are you two fucking scumbags? I'm calling the police right now if you don't come out.' We stay where we are—sniggering—and twenty minutes later we hear his vehicle churn into action and leave our happy home behind.

Sucker for your teenage ass

In Babylon, on the boulevard of broken dreams…
—Blondie

I still go down Old Street when I'm in London because these days it's the big nightclub area where all the fit pussy hangs out.

They've opened up the 666 Club where there used to be this fag bar and they've got JUJU around the corner from 666 where the Asian dance music revolution began, middled, and ended. Last year I saw the leader of the Zulu Nation, Afrika Bambaataa, DJing at JUJU; this year I caught Dee Dee Ramone acoustic at 666. So it's the terminally funky part of town now. Also it's where all the designers, the admakers, the chi chi arts and crafts crowd, the wankers want to live.

Back then it was an immense neutral hellhole, ill-lit and dangerous. I only visited there in the winter, the cold wet winters of cocaine and speed when Nigel Preston was a part of my life, and our prime exhibit. Nigel broke London for me and Jesse, and we've been cursed in our friendship by the commercial success Nigel gave us by throwing himself onto the pyre. Then Subliminal Kids were happy unknowns with neither money nor prospects but we were the best of friends. Now we've got everything London can give—but nothing else. Now Nigel is just a showbiz routine that made us famous, a bit of fascinating anecdotage to be trotted out immorally.

Sigue Sigue Sputnik—the band Subliminal Kids admired the most—were making their historic asshole assault on the ruins of the once-mighty English rock establishment, borrowing the dangerous and potent techniques of sampling, guitars and make-up, applying those methods to a musical form—rock'n'roll—then on its last legs. I loved Sigue Sigue from the moment I first heard of them and saw their pictures in the press.

I'd see them driving through Soho in their Rolls Royce, demented sluts born out of time, the last punks in town, psychotic androgynes. They came and went like lightning but their music lived on forever on our squat turntables. T Rex and a drum machine were all they needed to crack that scene.

In '89 it was cheapo wine. Jesse hooked us up with one particular posse firmly rooted in the Notting Hill junk'n'roll scene. I'm not sure who knew who, who screwed who, or where it all began. But it never ended.

It was that kind of intense drug time in my life—we thought that we were gods. I was penniless but money was never a real problem when it came to buying a little piece of mind.

Everything happened on the fringe of a rock band scene dominated by Thee Fanatics and The Bellreeves, intelligent practitioners of traditional rock music in a country grown tired and embarrassed by that art form. Those bands and the posses who hung out with them read good books, liked movies so much they never went to the cinema any more, and listened to uncompromised music.

The men in The Bellreeves—unacknowledged white outsiders from Jewish or Catholic backgrounds—came from newtowns just up the motorway from London, miles from anywhere in terms of where England was heading.

Coming from a newtown was obviously like coming from Ireland; you spent the first seventeen years of your life with nothing happening: waiting for something to happen, doing nothing and thinking about music all the time. Next you moved to Notting Hill and everything started happening: you were waiting for something to happen, doing nothing and thinking about music all the time.

Drugs came between The Bellreeves and stardom, but narcotics protected them from the harsh reality of Thatcher's England. Their names in lights were obscured by the cocaine clouds and the mightier clouds of psychic dust from heroin and whatever the wind just blew in. Some of those dudes were pretty, some of them were ugly, none of them ever got to where they wanted to go. I think they wanted to keep success a fantasy, whereas Subliminal Kids were determined to make it a reality.

I was closest to The Bellreeves' guitar player, a rockist statement called Dave Levy. Dave played guitar like he was ringing a bell. He didn't *sound* the equal of all those classic rock guitar legends, he was one of them—only they were millionaires and Dave was a penniless junkie prince.

One of many well hung Keith Richards clones, with

big pussy-eating lips, a perfect tiny ass and lingering pale blue eyes, he deserved to be a bad influence on the young generation. Jesse always wanted to recruit Levy into the Kids but Levy was profoundly loyal to his friends in The Bellreeves. This loyalty was commendable, the ultimate quality you need in a band member, but The Bellreeves had bad problems in both the drugs and management departments. The Bellreeves are still together **out** of loyalty; they just moved from Notting Hill to Nothing Hill.

It's not like the crack that you put in a pipe.

Natalie Starbuck was a provocation at the centre of a Thee Fanatics fringe scene very heavily into degeneration. These people gathered at the weekend in an Old Street club called Creation. Natalie had a man who hung out with her all the time—Larry—who may or may not have been her boyfriend; an essential ingredient of their two-hander routine was the hiding of all tangible facts. Natalie said she was the daughter of a retired admiral in the English Navy who lived somewhere naval on the south coast. Larry's old man was allegedly a professor of geography. They shared a cool-as-ice basement flat just off the Portobello Road.

Sometimes we reckoned that they were shagging. Sometimes we didn't have a clue. They successfully obscured their thinking, their motives, their lives.

Larry was a hale and hearty strapping lad in his early

73

twenties, a likable conversationalist without too much personality. He managed Thee Fanatics, totally OTT Catholic junkies living on Dead End Street, and he drove around town on a Harley Davidson. During the time that we hung with that set Thee Fanatics were always about to go on the road supporting Ozzy Ozbourne or some reactionary superstar. Nothing ever came of these plans, and Thee Fanatics were always to be found on Portobello Road during the week, or at Creation on the weekends.

Natalie Starbuck was very very thin and very beautiful, a pre-Raphaelite blonde cunt wearing lots of funky Parisian clothes which—blah, blah, blah—she picked up second hand all over town; just that none of those dresses, blouses, or silk scarves sagged or frayed like used clothes are supposed to. She had this rap that she was fighting leukemia with six months to live. This was communicated to you confidentially because she didn't want people to know about it because she didn't want to be treated like a victim because she only had six months to live so she wanted to live life to the full while she still could. Yabba, yabba, yabba.

Starbuck wasn't quite at the near-death stage yet. Plunging into a big long line of speed she'd regale me with stories about how the leukemia caused her massive pain and how she was heading off the following morning to a private clinic where she'd endure abominable procedures so horrific that they appeared almost Victorian or even Medieval.

We were just kids so we swallowed her bullshit. How could she look so good—tits, ass, hair—and feel so bad?

Patriarchal Good Guy that he was, Larry forbade Natalie from taking stuff like speed or cocaine that might exacerbate her condition. He'd whisper to us at Creation 'Don't give Natalie speed no matter what she says to you. It's really bad for her.' And she whispered to us at Creation 'Don't tell Larry I'm taking speed. He's really worried about me and he'd kill me if he knew.' The meantime, it was blissfully clear to all the boys in all the bands that Starbuck wandered through Creation out of her box on amphetamines and opiates, the very picture of robust British health with only months to live. The only pathetic consolation she got was from the drugs.

Creation took place in an uninhabited warehouse zone behind Old Street tube, lost in miles and miles of mercantile Victorian architecture, situated in the basement of a five-story redbrick. The ground floor was once a pub and the upper floors housed rag-trade related enterprises. The basement was, during the week, a working man's snooker hall, converted on Friday and Saturday nights into the nastiest filthiest club in London. The atmosphere was seriously masculine like you'd expect with a snooker hall, the air full of sweat, smoke and the rugged scheming of the disenfranchised.

Creation ran from after midnight all through the night until the trains ran again. They had four beefy nigger bouncers lurking under an ancient lamplight outside the basement door. So long as you looked dubious, bombed, dishonest, dirty or sicko they let you in.

Huddled around a rickety candle-lit table, one landing down, were flower children types who'd collect the admission from you or let you in with a nod depending on how out of it they were or what the vibe was. Another landing down, you walked right into the first of three small ill-lit rooms, each of which was capable of holding about one hundred people. You were in Creation.

It was never packed, the atmosphere was easy going and Creation was never a commercial club in any real sense. It existed so that drugs could be dealt. Booze wasn't sold on the premises and it didn't attract a drinking crowd. People were there to get high, to pick up one another and to forget the existential boredom of the weekend.

Larry and Natalie had something to do with the running of Creation—that was obvious because Natalie would occasionally confide: 'I'm never going to come here *ever* again. It's a real dump, isn't it?'

The men in charge were trendy enough individuals in their early twenties who'd worked out a deal with the outwardly benign East End gangster types who were always on the premises; well-built sexually neutral macho faggy boys dressed in their regulation Richardson Gang Bond Street suits.

Creation was a club free from club culture, a club for those that time was about to pass by.

The first room you came to played the rough end of the Sixties vision, the still-fresh undercooked punk inventions of the Stooges and the Velvet Underground. In that room the music came from urban sexual confusion, knife-edged alienation and the hedonism of the professional drugtaker.

The next room was the psychedelic zone where they played naff English stuff from the Sixties, soft-focus visions of non-existent nirvanas. This was the most popular room, a haven for middlebrow Brits who were one of Creation's constituencies; a middle room for middle people. Not me.

The third and inner room, the emptiest room, was where most of the drug taking went on and where the DJs played the American music of our time; I loved that sound and thought it was oh so terminally cool but now I'm not so sure.

Nobody'd been unplugged yet. The soundtrack was Jane's Addiction, Red Hot Chilli Peppers, Danzig, the then-ubiquitous Beastie Boys, lots of MTV alternative formatting. I thought Jane's Addiction were the real thing, that they were busy pushing back the boundaries of something other than their bank balances, pushing back the envelope. (Eventually Perry Farrell's despicable fat girlfriend moved into the big picture and all of a sudden the band was up to its neck in unimportance and junkie-style crisis.) The Chilli Peppers were great—a real band with a real lifestyle, a true story. The *Love Roller Coaster* thing they did for the Beavis and Butthead movie is great. My brain rides a skateboard.

Creation happened before the Beasties got boring and adult about the Dalai Lama—the Clinton-era CIA's pet project—while hanging out with John and Yoko's fucking son. I can see that the music has grown adult with them and is still good, but back in the days...let's just say I think they got off the skateboards.

In that back MTV room the thin girls hung out. Jesse and Nigel went there to be courted by amphetamine-fuelled A&R bitches from Warner Brothers while I was so out of it that I'd sit on the cold concrete floor alone in that zone of my own or else chatting with a sympathetic soul like Philippe. I really liked Philippe, he let me inside himself when I was in the mood for mind-fucking. That French boy was free with his psychic favours, a soul slut.

Natalie Starbuck would flit through the inner room searching for powders, spreading salacious gossip that I couldn't make sense of. I was just happy to be there, a denizen of the dark lonely corridor of uncertainty.

Our European religion was dead. I felt that any escape, any time, day and night, was good. I was a nighttown boy, and the nighttown boy don't need no invitation—he gets his lovin' on the run. Doing crack, cocaine and heroin was to be a low level freedom fighter. Prior to my time in Berlin, the most drugs I ever took in my life I took at Creation.

That was our Saturday night ritual for nine months. It would begin with Nigel phoning in to say he wouldn't be joining us. He'd be at home with his folks for the weekend or he was staying in with his wife for the night. Later, about the time I'd have cooked dinner, heading towards midnight, he'd show up unannounced like it'd been all organised previously. He'd be a bit grumpy, having just escaped from the domestic embrace of family, until Jesse rolled a big doobie and we were all grooving to NWA or The Afros.

When Nigel had settled down, the soundtrack would change and I'd serve up dinner for six or seven; there were always some girls about or other band members. I'd phone LX in his squat across the way when the food was ready, some kind of sensible beef stew or roast chicken. He'd join us when he'd gussied himself up a bit with eyeliner and moisturiser, and we'd eat together like a family, for a band is a family of sorts.

In the middle of the night we'd send the girls home, play something rootsy—Johnny Cash or Bob Dylan, depending on what we were up to or what humour we were in—and then we'd hit the road to Creation.

There's isolating frost and ice everywhere so LX doubts very much that the Volvo will go.

I doubt very much that LX can stand up. I suppose he did some scag before joining us for food so he wants to stay home and catch the Westwood show on the TV through a purple haze. Nigel has the measure of LX, has some mighty telling insights into the boy when he's in the mood, so he takes control of the situation.

'Listen you little shit,' he laughs at LX, 'if it was a drugs run we were organising there'd be nothing wrong with the fucking Volvo.' To which LX haughtily and humpily replies: 'Yes, well, h'mm, for all intents and purposes what we are going on *is* a drugs run.'

Primitive little animal that he is, LX can defend himself when cornered.

So an hour later the bitches are disposed of and the men set off in the Volvo, Nigel and Jesse sitting in the back rolling the joints while LX drives and I navigate, which means I pass my time looking out the window, dedicated urban voyeur, a country boy recently arrived in town, hating London but loving to be loose in it.

Outside is Society. Here on the inside, outside is so far away. So very far.

LX wasn't bullshitting about the car and the Volvo finds it heavy going to do more than fifty miles an hour so we crawl inelegantly northwards.

'Which way we going?' I ask LX and he says we'll go up through Brixton, past the iniquities of Elephant & Castle, over the Thames by Westminster Bridge and down towards Old Street. LX hits us for petrol money, like he always does around this time. Preston, as usual, has nothing to contribute. Jesse puts in a fiver and I do the same. We pull in at the Shell station next door to the Labour Party headquarters and there is a general exodus into the shop for skins, fags, munchies, crisps, toffees.

It's a matter of Russian Roulette which bridge LX chooses to cross the Thames, it depends on how out of it he is or how recently he came off. Jesse hates it when we cruise anywhere near Parliament or Buckingham Palace or Downing Street because that government zone is rancid with Pigs twenty-four hours a day, nasty hard-nosed grizzly Pigs with lots of experience in fighting terrorism, nabbing the Irish, sniffing out untaxed clapped-out Volvos. I like cruising around there, I never cease to be impressed by that House of Commons part of town. I'm not impressed by their democracy or their strange sense of what is normal behaviour, but witnessing the end of an empire at close quarters while sitting in its capital city sure is interesting.

I hate that fucking poem by that wanker

Wordsworth, and we are anything but dull of soul moving remorselessly towards Creation.

At the bottom of the stairs three longhaired thin boys are huddled mysteriously in a corner, pretty vacantly staring at some grim old German horror movie flickering dimly onto a massive big screen. Hefty Goth girls and their much thinner boyfriends are wandering sadly; the girls all fretful, the men all tormented. A nice hippy couple are selling teas (mint tea, fruit tea, real tea) and coffees. The girl is a cutie, seventeen and seemingly kind-hearted. The boy, morose though genial, is younger than his girl. The room is saturated in dry ice and, psychologically speaking, gives the impression of being warm, just that there's not enough people here to heat things up. Couples are dancing in the mist and others do crazy solo dancing. The DJ is Dave Bellreeves and he is playing *Search and Destroy*, *Sweet Sixteen* and *I Wanna Be Your Dog* which is fucking profoundly original of him. The Bellreeves are joining the long parade to the graveyard.

I go down the long uncertain corridor leading to the Men's Room and as usual there are five guys queuing ahead of me and the stink of piss and puke is in bed with the dry ice and the hashish and they're making a big smelly baby. A young queer in front of me starts talking and he says he recognises me from Camden, which is possible, or which may be coded queer talk concerning some gay bar. Sure he has a nice face and baby it's cold outside so who knows? It's going to be a long night and I might get desperate later.

The reality is that I'm about to plunge into a night of reckless speed so I doubt very much that Little Kim will be coming out to play tonight.

I'm moving through the crowd and the leather's all around me. I'm just hangin' around. I'm in the back room and it's hello to Natalie who is with this beautiful drug slut, a Jewish Princess from the Island A&R department. So it's *Hi* and *Good to meet ya* and I'm out of there.

OK, I have these band-managerial responsibilities to the Kids and I should be talking with the bitch about business but if she's so fucking all powerful in the Soho showbiz scene, what the fuck is she doing in the middle of the night in this drug den listening to this crematorium rock when she could be grooving to House on the other side of town? Before I leave the room, my idea of small talk is to ask Miss A&R if she'd like a line but she goes all London on me and says she never takes the stuff so I say to her 'Oh, well, some people rarely touch it but it touches them, like Tennessee Williams says.'

And therefore Subliminal Kids will not be duetting with U2 or feeding the fucking world in the near future.

I'm looking for the guys but they've communally disappeared and who appears out of the smog but the queer from the toilet? He's talking about Ibiza and Goa which is not my scene but at least he's talking about dance music so I ask him if he wants another line and we're off to the amenities again. In the bog he keeps on nattering on about Ibiza and I say to him 'Do you think that scene will last?' and he says 'Yeah, well, why not? It'll last forever, no reason why not. I mean, look at Christianity, that's lasted forever.'

Twenty minutes later I get back to the dancefloor and the Kids have made a comeback: Jesse is chatting with the Island bitch, Nigel has nodded off, and LX is surrounded by a gang of women.

Philippe, I didn't know he was going to be here tonight or we could have given him a lift, spots me and comes over.

'Hey Kim! What's happening?' he says.

'Nothing just yet. I've just run out of speed. I need to score some. What's happening?'

'Very little. I got some speed here. What do you say to visiting the toilette with me and we can share mine. I just bought it from the tall guy over there who says he knows you.' Philippe points at Larry who sees Philippe pointing and salutes me.

'Hats off to Larry, then,' I say, wired and frustrated, grinding my teeth, inhaling the dry ice, stumbling into a velveteen drape hanging down from a dividing wall and hating all the people I know in the room individually and collectively, getting into the tune that is playing—

Masters of Reality—hating myself, my wretched insincere shallow self for hanging around with men when I want to hang around with women and the women here could happen for me only I'm too perplexed to do anything about it.

We leave at dawn. Snow has fallen while we've been inside so everywhere is bright and white when our bruised eyes behold the day. Jesse looks at me, mischievously accusatory, says 'I saw you were keeping poor company.'

I put my arm around his shoulders and I tell him 'You know, they come up to me, I don't go up to them.'

Something like a phenomenon

My name is Kim, called after Kim Il Sung, the North Korean leader.

When I was a teenager I got sent a copy of Kim's three volume official biography in which it says: 'Even the midday sun itself had lost its lustre when Generalissimo Kim Il Sung, incomparable leader of the international working class and proletarian movement, came upon the scene.' I kind of liked that so I changed my name to Kim. My Dad christened me William after his Dad, and I was known as Bill until I was seventeen.

It's 2AM and I'm in the Coldharbour Lane apartment

of DJ Found while his girlfriend Erika—an architecture student—is out working in a Notting Hill nightclub. Even though she knows that I am here, our meeting is in some way secret, as if she doesn't understand what we really get up to. They are a very strange couple and I don't know exactly where their agenda begins and ends.

I walked all the way down here after midnight, via the dole office, via the Barrier Block, illegally picking up a six-pack in Zambezi Cafe, a late-night dive full of rastas and minicab drivers. There was a poster in the window for the roots dub Aba Shanti I Sound System and smoky dub reggae blasting out of an ancient ghetto blaster behind the counter.

Found is an East German boy, child of the non-materialistic world with a funny 19th Century sense of humour, a Romantic in the mode of Goethe and Schiller. Sometimes when he is just too stoned he thinks the world is divided into a man's world and a woman's world. He has a certain point and this evening we are playing a man's game in a "man's world". The flat is Erika's doing with all her warm comfort, sensible German shoes in every room, her architectural drawings everywhere.

He stands with his back to me now, concentrating on his two turntables, his sampler and his reel-to-reel. He says that art begins with two turntables, not an original idea but an obscure one. Found knows so much more about this new music than me that, untypically, all I can do is shut up and listen. Found, who can be childish or cerebral by turn, hands me a heavy-duty essay written in German which I can't read on Faust, Stockhausen, architecture and Kraftwerk.

The music Found makes mixes new dance beats—the rave music they advertise in Soho with beautiful full colour flyers—with TV dialogue, the taped conversations of old girlfriends, Erika talking to him while the two of them are in bed together, Communistic American folk singers, negro prisoners breaking rocks in the Southern penitentiary, awful East German heavy rock groups, the voices coming through the tannoy out at Heathrow, the first TV ads he heard in his first London flat. He is creating an autobiographical aural sculpture chronicling his emergence from the cocoon of East Germany into the light of seeing the Wall come down, and on and on to moving to London, the very heart of the free market. The music he creates, melodic enough in its intellectual way, is totally new to me and I'm impressed.

'Kim you are a very smart man and your friend Jesse is smart too,' Found says, taking a break from music making, his Germanic accent making him sound strident and emphatic, 'but you'll get old if you don't pay attention to what's happened to music and sound since the Seventies. Your whole civilisation is on tape today.

President Reagan, Andy Warhol, your Rolling Stones, everything you saw and heard when you were a child was seen and heard by the universe. There is a universal soundtrack. Tape memory is human memory and I believe that tape memory will replace composition.'

Erika phones in just then and they talk in German. I don't understand anything but I hear the exasperation in his voice and I hear my own name mentioned several times.

'Is Erika on her way home?' I ask Found when he eventually gets off the phone.

'No. She wanted to come home but I told her that you were here so she is going back to a friend's place for a while. I told her we were doing important work.' With this he turns back to the tapes and the turntables.

I lie on their big springy double bed reading Vogue, listening to the music he's writing and occasionally glancing at the television where some disgusting TV movie is happening.

At dawn I decide I better go before Erika gets home. I leave him caught up in his own world of composition while hard working people are making their way to work on Coldharbour Lane. I'm slow going back towards Brixton but elated with the music I've seen and heard being written in front of my worried-about-the-future eyes. I know that guitar rock is fundamentally challenged, but I still love it; I also know that logical alternatives like Found might blitzkrieg my world and wipe out my culture.

I forget all that lofty stuff when I reach Zambezi Cafe where I bought the six-pack hours earlier. It's cordoned off and dozens of paranoid looking Pigs, some of them quite senior, are standing everywhere conferring with one another and talking into walkie talkies. The cafe is sealed off by crime scene tape. There's a little blood on the footpath, somebody got murdered, but otherwise everything is the same as when I was in there earlier. In my crotch I'm carrying a little grass that Found gave me as a farewell gift so I move along quick enough.

When I get home I'm so shagged that I want to crash right away but Jesse is watching breakfast TV with his girlfriend and he calls me into the sitting room, where the local news has just reported a fatal stabbing in a Brixton cafe. I tell them that it happened on Coldharbour Lane and that I've just been at the scene of the crime. Jesse's girlfriend doesn't want to hear about it and heads for their bedroom.

'They said it was a drug related killing?' Jesse says.

'I was in the fucking place late last night, man. I went in there to get a six pack and there were just a few dudes sitting around.'

'Where were you going?' Jesse asks drily.

'I was on my way down to see Found.'

'That asshole.'

'Well, you don't have to like him…'

'I don't.' Jesse turns off the TV with the remote control and leaves the room.

Firebomb Telecom

My pal the art dealer Lowry offers to take me with him on a business trip to Manchester. I have to get to his Knightsbridge flat at 7.30AM, the time I usually go to sleep. He says I'm welcome to come along if I want to.

This morning I get to Knightsbridge on time. After a good quick breakfast we hit the motorways. Four miles out of London, at 8.30, we grind to a halt in a traffic jam and it doesn't unfurl for almost an hour.

'Christ!' I say, full of that wretched I-want-to-be-in-bed feeling. 'It's amazing what these people go through every day. It's fascinating to think that there's this whole subculture exists out here on the motorways.'

'This is not a fucking subculture, Kim,' Lowry says calmly. 'This is life!'

Lowry is a client for the free phones. He pays a tenner an hour to use the phone in LX's place, doing dodgy art business with middle ranking civil servants in crumbling East European states like Bulgaria and Albania. He sells a lot of art from that neck of the woods—I guess he must be getting it from somewhere! Lowry has extensive connections with Polish and other East European cabals across London. He knows lots of restaurants in South Ken and North London where you can get cabbagey and porky East European delicacies. I guess it's a kind of Catholic ambience that appeals to the both of us.

When Lowry has an art opening, the wine's invariably East European, as are the busty flirty waitresses filling the glasses of would-be punters. He's trying to marry me off to a Polish girl whose boyfriend is in jail back home for being in Solidarity. Her EEC visa is up, which means she'll have to abandon Knightsbridge and go home to greasy bacon and black bread unless she gets married. It's a paying gig, like the showbands used to say, so I'm on for it. I overheard him on LX's phone yesterday saying he knew a man in Geneva who's trying to sell a lake full of live carp, and that he—Lowry—is authorised to sell these fish!

Lowry says the East Europeans, especially the Polish, are phenomenally resourceful people who stay awake at night, tossing and turning, trying to think up ways to thwart the system. Via one such Polish connection Lowry brought us the silver foil scam, now the principal weapon at the disposal of Operation Firebomb Telecom.

They got this silver-backed duct tape used by electricians to seal in their work, with a powerful adhesive on the other side. When cut in the shape of a 10p coin and stuck to the coin, the added weight makes it register as

50p on most vending machines. It works the best on telephones, but also on train ticket vending machines and stamp machines. Last night we made hundreds of 50p pieces with the foil and we set to work. LX drove us to every stamp machine in South London. We collected enough stamps to keep us going for six months. Today we all bought weekly tube Travelcards. This morning I heard by phone about vending machines selling £10 Phonecards. They'll make it even easier to Firebomb Telecom, doing long distance phonecalls from the coinbox in front of Tulse Hill Estate.

The powers-that-be are on to the foil. Electrical supply shops are being visited by Pigs and advised to ask people buying the foil exactly what they're purchasing it for.

Lowry heard about the scam from a gang of disgruntled Polish nuclear scientists who hang out in an East European club he goes to near Regent's Park. They researched the scam themselves and deserve one of those free market awards for ingenuity.

Bunk

The upstairs neighbours were niggers, a young couple. Bunk was about nineteen and very beautiful. Carrie was sixteen and had a somewhat undernourished, sickly aspect to her.

Bunk made money every day dealing on his mobile phone and making deliveries in his jeep. He spent his money stupidly—like the boy that he really was—on designer clothes and flashy toys. In front of our block he parked the slick new Toyota jeep where he passed most of his afternoons. Bunk hated our Volvo, the fact that we parked it alongside his car, what it said about us, what it said about him, and where we were all coming from. He'd block our path while we were getting into the Volvo, orate about how he was in charge of his own life and how he didn't give a fuck about anybody else. He said he paid all his bills, had a good life, that we never paid our bills and were leading worthless lives.

Carrie would sit in the jeep while this ranting was in progress, her eyes totally blank and her head nodding agreement with whatever bullshit her man happened to come up with at any given moment.

Bunk's problem was that he self-evidently wanted to come out to play with us, for us to tell him what nice toys he had, for us white boys to be his pals. He had big mature cock-sucking lips that quivered nervously when he spoke. Since he came on so cheeky, disrespectful and aggressive, I'd smile at him lewdly when he tried to get in my way. When my smile had his attention I'd let my eyes drift down to his crotch where they'd linger for a moment before I mentally undressed him, looked him straight in the eye again, making sure that he knew that

I knew that he knew that I was objectifying him like that.

He liked sexual attention so his belligerent outbursts usually ran out of steam, rancour giving way to petulance and then to spitefulness. His skin was more off-white than black and he was a real heartbreaking china doll.

My bedroom was right under their bedroom, meaning that I heard everything going on above me. When I'd be going to sleep by the dawn's early light, I'd hear him sticking like a cactus, bouncing like a mattress. This normally took about three minutes and was little more than a quick wank at her expense. Carrie was permanently out to lunch, her motor responses were severely limited at the best of times. I could hear everything so clearly that I might as well have been in the room there with them, sitting in the middle of their bed. I caught every *Oh!* or *Move that fucking pillow!* or *Stop for a second, would ya?* When he came he'd go *Oh! Oh!* a few times and there'd be silence. He'd eventually revive, start talking at her, complain how hard he worked to give them a good home, how dirty the place always was, how she was just a slag and why didn't she try to make herself look better for him. A regular theme was how much money he had and nasty stuff about her mother. He'd calm down and they'd sleep. Me too. I'd even smoke a fag on their behalf.

I could tell from the way he looked at me during the daytime hours that he knew I was aware of their private life in this intimate detail. I think he liked it that I was in on their action, that I knew how often he got laid, that I heard what he said to his fuck-bag. In theory he was a nasty macho nigger cocksucker with too much arrogant attitude. In fact we were neighbours and our lives fed off of one another.

One day Bunk got into some heavy philosophical shit while we were having our usual argument about LX parking the Volvo in Bunk's space.

'You know, you guys come here to my country,' he shouted, 'you don't work…you scrounge off the dole. You should be ashamed of yourselves, all the opportunities God has given you. I work hard all day to support my woman.'

'My friend,' I said smiling, walking towards him. 'This is *not* your country. You may have been born here but this is *not* your country. They do *not* want you here. Before they brought you niggers here, we Irish were their niggers.'

The mention of the word *nigger* made him wince, as it did all blacks and most whites. But I was not prepared to compromise. As far as I was concerned I was a nigger too. The Irish are the only white people ever colonised by a European colonial power. Under the Penal Laws that the English enforced on Ireland back in the days, a

Catholic (i.e. native Irish) couldn't own land, vote, or possess a horse worth more than a fiver. Sound familiar? Yes, we see.

When blacks would object to me using *nigger* I'd explain my thinking to them. They generally took it in bad grace while accepting that my explanation had some validity. When whites took exception I'd joke: 'I prefer to call a spade a spade.' If they belly laughed I knew they were racists. If they chuckled whimsically or dubiously, I knew they were possibly OK. The people who gave you the most grief were middle class whites of profoundly privileged background, who'd never chatted with, eaten with, or fucked with a nigger in their entire lives. The people who gave me the least grief were niggers I was hanging with.

Bunk took it on the chin and let it pass, not as truculent as he let on.

'My dad came from Santa Lucia,' he said, calming down. 'My mum was a teacher there. She took a job as a seamstress when she got here.'

'Exactly,' I said. 'I'm a historian. Here everybody thinks I'm a builder.'

'My dad is a big jazz fan,' Bunk said, getting into his jeep and turning on his radio. 'He called me Bunk after a jazz musician called Bunk Johnson.'

'I reckoned.'

'What?'

'I reckoned you were called after Bunk Johnson.'

'You've heard of him?'

I was probably the first white boy he'd ever encountered who knew the music of the man who did the finest version of *When The Saints Go Marching In*.

'I want to be in that number…' I mimicked, and china doll Bunk finally smiled.

'My mum is crazy, you know,' he confided as he prepared to drive away. 'She goes to church twice on Sundays. She goes in the morning, comes home and gets lunch for Dad, and then she's back praying for the afternoon.'

He had my complete attention with his curly brown hair, his boy's ass, his passionate brown eyes. I heard him coming every morning and sometimes he heard me coming too.

His noise wasn't exclusively of sex; a lot of the time I could hear him hammering, sawing, doing timber work, moving furniture around the room. The china doll was always moving his stash someplace new in the flat, putting his gear under the floorboards, behind concealed holes in the wall. Then, often later that very same day, crack would take hold of Bunk's soul and he'd forget where he'd stashed his stuff or, alternatively, conclude that his hiding place was unsafe, that he needed a new one. Three or four times a week he'd go completely psycho and tear his pad apart looking for his crack.

After a while, when the searching was over, he'd start rebuilding his home from scratch.

It's too hot for sleep and I'm still coming down from whatever I took at Creation. Sunday morning coming down. I'm not sure what I took. Jesse says to me and he's right: 'Some guy hands you two pills and you don't have a clue what they are and you swallow them just like that.' To which I reply ungratefully: 'Yeah?'

I woke from my drug-light sleep twenty minutes ago, roused by noise from Bunk's flat upstairs. Sometimes the way he looks at me makes me call him Strange Fruit and come to think of it he bears a passing resemblance to Billie Holliday. But he sure don't sound like Billie Holliday just now, he sounds more like Little Richard, screaming like a stuck pig. The noise he is making is nothing compared with all the other uproar trespassing into my morning. The bitch is screaming too, somebody is smashing wood with hatchets, glass is breaking, and Billie Holliday is howling *Fuck. Oh fuck. Fuck!* The other voices are white English ones and next thing I hear is walkie-talkies so I understand just what is happening. The Pigs are doing a raid and it's every man for himself.

I pull on a pair of jeans, zip myself up, go to the kitchen to make some coffee, abandoning all hope of sleep or even security. I turn on the shitty old Sony radio to GLR and there's a Gospel show. I turn it up good and loud to drown out the upstairs mayhem but I guess, even though she's just a stupid drugged cunt and he's merely a beneath-contempt little he-goat, I feel very sorry for them. If my consciously cool stance of going to live amongst the niggers means anything, it means that we stand together against Babylon, and those two are suffering at the hands of Babylon right now.

I take my mug of coffee and go into the sitting room which is a total mess, band posters everywhere, albums out of their sleeves. I'm living like a criminal, a criminal I be. If Jesse was here right now he'd be flushing skins down the toilet and wanting to throw little bits of shit away in case the Pigs raid us too but Jesse is elsewhere with others. I can't relax, the noise has been going on for twenty minutes that I know of. I walk out onto the landing and look down to see eight Pig cars and two vans. One or two officers wander through the yard, talking into walkie talkies while staring at the upper stories of my building, taking note of such as me. I look up and I see very little but I can hear a lot, mainly Billie Holliday delivering a pretty good line in abuse while his Carrie sobs and cries.

For sure we're in the Deep Ellum blues of Darktown now.

I go inside to refill my mug, get caught up in a holy tune, and by the time I'm back on the landing it's all over. Pigs are pouring out of the ground floor stairwell and the lift. Two of them are restraining a handcuffed Bunk, who is struggling like the emotional fool that he is. He gets pushed into the back seat of a car without a problem. They've got baggies full of whatever and a few cardboard boxes of 'evidence'. Like a funeral procession the whole lot of them cruise out of Tulse Hill Estate as I go upstairs to investigate.

Carrie is standing in her doorway dazed, all cuts and bruises. She looks at me pathetically before inviting me inside. Their home must have been great before the Pigs started—didn't know you could spend £10,000 in Woolworths—but now it's just a sad pile of rubble. All the ridiculous Scandinavian black leather couches have been slashed open, the colour TVs in every room are smashed and violation has made the place uninhabitable.

'You want to come downstairs for a joint?' I ask her.

Carrie nods her agreement, she is saying very little.

So I bring her downstairs, give her a coffee and roll a doobie. While we're sharing it she tells her story.

'They kicked in the door while we were in bed together lovin',' she says slowly, evenly, 'two of them held me down on the mattress and punched me and kicked me about a while. I was naked...so was Buck...so this big dyke pulls me about on the ground by my hair. They pins Buck to the ground, put on rubber gloves, and three of them search his ass. He was bleeding and crying and it was stupid, fucking stupid. Then they done all that...'

She is silent for ten minutes during which I say nothing. A choir is singing *Go Tell It On The Mountain* on the radio. When she is good and ready she keeps on going.

'There were so many of them in there. Then they started kicking Buck all over the place too, calling him an ugly little nigger, hitting him across the head with their truncheons, kicking him in the balls, tearing up photographs of his mother, it just went on and fucking on and there were twenty of them. The dyke was enjoying it and she done the body search on me when she was ready. When they were finished with Buck they started looking for our gear which was hidden all over the fucking place. When they found it they were happy and they took him away from me. They took him away from me.'

The last sentence said so pitifully.

Go tell it on the mountain
Set my people free.
Go tell it on the mountains
Set my people free.
Who's that yonder dressed in red?
Must be the children that Moses lead.
Who's that yonder dressed in white?

Must be the children of the Israelites.
Go tell it on the mountain
Set my people free.
Go tell it on the mountains
Set my people free.

Pigs

I was passing Patel's newsagents when I saw the commotion caused by three carloads of police. Inside the shop Patel and the Pigs were gathered around the security monitors, their eyes glued to a full colour video playback. The image-definition of the footage was superb, and—through the window—I saw what had happened on the TV monitors before I saw the awful reality, before anybody filled me in on the sequence of events.

When I'd gotten the general idea off the monitors I walked inside the shop and nobody tried to stop me. No scene-of-the-crime tape blocked the entrance, no paranoid eyes followed me. Back of the shop, sitting dazed as a moron on the ground, was this young black man with blood pouring from the side of his shaved head, white stuff dribbling from his mouth. A small old black woman wearing a bright red jumpsuit bent over him, trying to stem the tide of blood with some paper napkins. Other black women gathering near her were saying that she should leave him alone and wait for the ambulance to show up: 'It's futile, my dear, it's futile.'

His eyes were open and those terrifying eyes darted all over the shop. I don't think he could really see or hear what was going on for his brain was already fading and he was a goner.

I walked through the shop in a daze myself. With Patel and his four sons preoccupied with the murder, with the surveillance cameras turned off, with the Pigs having something better to think about, I slipped over to where Patel kept the music magazines and stuffed *The Face*, *Spin* and *Mondo 2000* inside my leather jacket. While grabbing the magazines—other youths were grabbing their choices at the very same moment—I listened to the nigger conversations.

The man now dying on the floor had just been minding his own business, buying milk and chocolate biscuits for his wife, when this asshole crackhead walked into the shop and found the victim getting between him and the till. The cracker took a twelve-inch metal bar from inside his jacket and he whacked the sad fucker across the back of the head. Just for good measure, as the man was swaying and about to fall to the ground, the crackhead got in a second whack on the side of the head. After this display Patel, dazed and terrified, opened his till and gave the thief its contents.

I peered in between the shelves at the wounded man, a tragic little father dressed in impeccably tidy poor-folks threads, except for the blood that was falling onto everything. He probably didn't know he was about to die, just lay there, too dumb, sick and scared to work anything out for himself. He moaned quietly, beyond consolation. The good part of me felt like saying *Don't worry, Brother, you're really the lucky one, soon the suffering will all be over for you.* Instead I went back to where the Pigs were watching the monitors. They kept rerunning over and over again the bit where the crackhead struck the first blow. The metal came down on the shaved skull and matter exploded everywhere, fountains of blood erupted all over the place. From time to time a tired middle aged Pig, tall and paunchy, looked over his shoulder at the dying man and then back to the screen. None of the Pigs went over to see if he was OK or to give proper first aid. I heard it through the grapevine, i.e. from one of the old nigger women, that an ambulance was on its way. Just about to lose my mind.

Patel was anxious to get back to trading, to stop the low-key looters from having a field-day. An eleven year old skate kid, blonde and bony, the son of an American squatter couple I knew vaguely, wearing a t-shirt with the word PUBERTY printed across his chest, gave me a fraternal wink as he stuffed pricey comics into his Nike shoulder bag.

When the ambulance finally arrived the Pigs started behaving like humans and three female officers, all stiff, grave and responsible came over to chat with the ambulance staff, to explain in pert white man's terms—professional to professional—what had happened. The paramedics, knowing he was a goner, gave the victim a quick once over, rolled out a stretcher, gently placed him on it and removed the embarrassment.

The Patels of England were the heroes of the Thatcher revolution, recently arrived from Nigeria without a pot to piss in; now they were making fortunes selling cheap envelopes, Rizla papers and pitta bread to vermin like me. The Pigs were just social binmen, cleaning up the shop for Patel so he could get back to the business of free market capitalism.

I phoned Jesse to tell him what I'd seen and that I was heading up town for the evening. I'd gotten my dole and I loved to blow it in one day, preferably on records. I was in the middle of an extended period of solitary pleasure. I didn't have a girlfriend, Jesse was barely on talking terms with me and all my so-called friends were abroad.

I went to a late night used record shop north of Oxford Street where I sometimes picked up overpriced vintage stuff. A smart old queen I'd never talked to was serving behind the counter, talking to an ex-Mod about Jimmy Smith records. After a while the conversation moved on to this very expensive Animals album that the

Mod was thinking about buying. I chipped in that I'd seen Eric Burdon in concert in Amsterdam the previous summer and that it was a travesty.

After the Mod and me talked for a few minutes he decided to buy the Animals record, and paid for it with his credit card. As he made to leave he turned to me and said: 'I've given up wearing the clothes. I've retired. In any case, I've always said that you either buy the clothes or you buy the records.'

The women and the crack

Oh, Mary this London's a wonderful sight,
People here working by day and by night.
They don't grow potatoes or barley or wheat,
But there's gangs of them digging for gold in the street.
At least when I asked them that's what I was told,
So I just took a hand in this digging for gold.

Jesse: Fitz brought me up to a party at his old Willesden squat last night and I got totally fucked up…They were playing some really shit music, really naff, and this chick got raped by four of them…
Kim: Fitz? Did Fitz join in the fun?
Jesse: Yeah, I'm sure he did. I mean…being Fitz…why not? I only heard about it afterwards.

Kim: Those fucking Aussies are savages, man, with their fucking AC/DC and all that shit.

Jesse: Not half the savages the Irish are. In the middle of the night this pitched battle started between the Wexford guys who were living there and these Mayo bogtrotters who were at the party and who had some notion that they had a territorial claim—not on the entire squat, not on the parts occupied by the Aussies or the South Africans—but very specifically, on the Wexford wing.

Kim: Who are bogtrotters too, all those Wexford cretins.

Jesse: Yeah, we are the boys of Wexford. Anyway, in the middle of the night while I was a bit preoccupied after hearing about the rapo-pillage...

Kim: You were going to be the knight in shining armour and save the damsel in distress.

Jesse: I guess I would have but it was all over by then and three women had already rescued her...the action had moved elsewhere...thirty Mayo men showed up down in the Wexford quarters which were deserted because most everybody was at the party or elsewhere. Two queer Wexford boys were getting it on, cat's away and the mice will play, when the mucky Mayo horde marched in, wielding sticks, knives and other stuff. They kicked in the door where the queers were getting it on.

Kim: Two hairy fellows crawling all over each other.

Jesse: Not so hairy really, they were teenagers, but my story ain't quite funny. The Mayo assholes were outraged, naturally, at the sight of such depravity...

Kim: At the mere thought of anybody having a good time.

Jesse: So they set upon the two boys, left one of them with really fucking serious injuries. Broke an arm, a leg, ribs, punched in his teeth. The other homo, the one on top, was able to fend them off in the end, I don't know the details. In the meantime the rednecks started throwing clothes and stereos and shit out the windows, smashing the glass in the windows, making enough noise to attract attention away from the party. First the Wexford posse, their pals and their chicks marched down the street to reclaim their home and attack the Mayo crew. Five minutes later everybody else joined in; shillelagh law did then ensue. The Pigs showed eventually, hauled everybody apart, busted a pile of people, got ambulances. The queer is in intensive care and one of the Mayo fuckers who got thrown out of a third floor window is paralysed for life. Luckily the Pigs stayed in the Wexford wing, well away from where I was.

In like Sean Flynn

I read this article in a tabloid Sunday paper colour supplement about an apartment in Paris that belonged to Sean Flynn.

In my punk phase I was a big Clash fan so I knew

exactly who Sean Flynn was: the glamorous son of Errol Flynn who proved to be a righteous aggressive photographer in Vietnam during the war and who disappeared without a trace only to be immortalised in Michael Herr's book *Dispatches* and a song by The Clash.

Flynn is the River Phoenix of Vietnam, the sexy weird hip one with the compelling image of universal and timeless appeal. Time has not dated Sean Flynn who died pretty, a perfect icon. Extravagant Jim Morrison-style legend suggests that he went native, that he was so stoned, cool and leftist in the most bombed country in the world that he fell in love with the people of Vietnam, abandoning his work, his Daddy's fortune, our entire white civilisation to go live with some voluptuous Vietnamese bitch dressed in a straw hat in a straw hut in a paddyfield or something. (The reality was recently discovered—he just got executed by the Viet Cong).

The colour supplement feature reported a rediscovered apartment in Paris where Sean Flynn used to live when not away on assignment. The pad originally belonged to Errol Flynn, was presumably his Parisian love shack, and was inherited by Sean in the fullness of time. Given the uncertainties surrounding Sean's disappearance, his estate didn't get wound down immediately and nobody went into the flat until 1989. When they finally opened the place they found a time capsule abandoned by a busy rich young hipster in his prime, allowing us a strange glimpse not only into Flynn's life but into that romantic epoch he inhabited.

There were his shades, Jefferson Airplane albums, his leather threads, his cameras, contact sheets, copies of *Rolling Stone*, love letters, rubbers, his stuff. Home is where the stuff is.

Jesse got a wicked squat for LX right across the way from our home. When we kicked in the front door, we walked into an ambience like that in Sean Flynn's place. Like the Flynn story, it reminded us that 'home' is an illusion. You can walk out the front door, walk away from the security and surety of home and never see that place again. We fantasize that home is real, that it will last forever, that we need it in our lives. Being nervous animals, we need homes. Home is where the normal heart is.

LX's new home had three bedrooms and a fancy kitchen full of Victorian cooking implements, ancient brass saucepans and a shelf of expensive cookery books. The presses were full of herbs, spices, wine and lots of dried pasta. The main bedroom had a huge double bed, all the rooms were painted in the contemporary Eighties shades. The apartment had big bookshelves in the living room, heating, an ancient bath and a spare bedroom full of books and magazines. From time to time Jesse regretted having given the place to LX and felt he should've moved there himself but, as was the normal deal with folks we got squats for, we maintained access to the place, installed phonelines for phone fraud in our own room and laid claim to a few nice bits of furniture.

The night Jesse broke in and changed the lock he had trouble opening the door because five months' worth of mail had collected on the ground under the letterbox. This pile was meat and potatoes to the left-over boiled-over historian in me so I spent happy hours going through it. I dumped three hundred pizza delivery flyers and other promotional shit, and then I was left with the story of the previous tenant's life.

His name was Nik Hunter. He was thirty-five, unmarried and worked as a film cameraman. There were five different letters offering him good work on film or TV dramas. These was one letter expecting him to show up on location in Prague the previous September to begin a six week shoot. Then there were follow-up letters wondering where the fuck he was. There were maybe forty Christmas cards from the previous winter. More than half were professional, corporate or otherwise impersonal. The rest came from friends, who divided roughly fifty/fifty into women and men.

Eighteen personal letters, again dividing fifty/fifty, contained the usual details of people's love lives, their travels, their travails at work. A lot of the mail was bills, their sequence beginning with polite requests for payment and ending with red threats of court action.

When Jesse discovered the flat no proceedings had yet begun, but in the fullness of time LX had to fend off several bailiffs come to collect on hefty debts. Along with the bills there were many kind offers of credit. We took advantage of as many of these offers as was humanly possible, and then some.

The most interesting room was the spare bedroom which Jesse claimed for us, containing back issues of *Time Out* and *The American Cinematographer* for the last five years. Hunter had every copy of *Rolling Stone* between 1979 and 1986. There were about three hundred paperback books there; most were science fiction and the more serious ones—though they were by no means all by queer writers—suggested that Nik was a fag (Bret Easton Ellis, Barbara Pym, Truman Capote, yabba, yabba, yabba). It took a month to go through all the publications in that room and it wasn't until I got to the very end that I found over two hundred very expensive gay porn mags containing the dirtiest stuff...lots of butt hair, lots of hole shots, penetration, underage boys being splayed by big hairy biker bears. We sold most of the porn to a Soho dealer. I held back about five juicy ones. The other journals and books travelled across town to the Record & Tape Exchange.

There was contradictory evidence too. Hunter disappeared, but not without premeditation. In the sitting room were fresh cardboard boxes, complete with Styrofoam packing, in which a pricey sound system had arrived, including a Technics turntable and huge Tannoy speakers, but there was no sign of this sound system. There was a teak TV table but no TV. The living room had wall-to-wall bookshelves but the bundles of yellowing paperbacks in the spare room had obviously not filled them. There were no photographs of Hunter, his family or friends, anywhere.

There were superb bits and pieces of clothes in the wardrobe, worn Ralph Lauren t-shirts and Levi jeans well past their sell-by date, yet one imagined that the many bare clothes hangers had once boasted slicker garments than the ones left behind.

Jesse said that one day LX would wake up to a loud bang on the front door and find an outraged Hunter standing there, just returned from six months on location in Morocco or someplace, having made some godawful mini-series starring Sophia Loren, Priscilla Presley and Larry Hagman, ready to resume normal life. That never happened and, over the years that he stayed there, LX came to rest easy.

In all that time not a single friend came to that front door looking for Nik Hunter, who'd obviously been socially active, professionally successful, and on the way up. His mail slowed up but never stopped coming. LX eventually lost the flat when Lambeth evicted him for non-payment of rent. I analysed the mail as it arrived and specific bits of evidence convinced me that I knew just what happened to Hunter.

He was a man of his time and the plague took him away. He went from HIV to AIDS, went into decline, eventually slunk off to a hospice to die. His closest friends removed his valuables and nobody said anything to anybody: AIDS was then the disease that dared not speak its name.

Do anything you wanna do

Falco was a brave German in a certain way. He did much better things when he was younger back in Germany. By the time Jesse came across him all those glories were in the recent past. His world had turned to shit, he knew it, and he was squatting on Tulse Hill too.

Falco must have been a real looker when he was a kid but he'd been in a bad motorcycle crash that completely crushed his left leg, causing him constant pain. He had a shitload of willpower so when the doctors told him he'd never have a normal life he refused their advice, did therapy and exercise to knock himself into shape. He didn't have any limp or visible sign of his injury. He was well built with long black hair, a sort of Germanic rock'n'roll fantasy on the dark streets of London.

He was doing his German Jack Daniels thing when he stumbled into our fantasy, living with a confused girlfriend called Amel who'd been with him since the Fatherland. Amel's father was a dealer so she grew up mean, shagging on the streets of Bonn from the age of twelve. She was a whole Lou Reed nightmare come to life in my home.

Amel and Falco had their own band—Texema—and rehearsed in the same Elephant & Castle studios as Subliminal Kids. Texema encapsulated Amel and Falco's long-term friendship, and things were working out fine for them. They got a long review in the *Melody Maker*, which was more than could be said for Subliminal Kids at the time. At first they scowled at us so we scowled right back at them, normal band behaviour, hostility is an intense form of attraction. I regret the destruction that ensued because, in retrospect, our mutual endeavours were not important to any of us.

The good part of Falco was burnt out and indifferent but that pessimism and hopelessness is part of the German make-up and sometimes, with the right encouragement, burnt out guitarists can be revived. We eventually got to talking because, after all, we shared a taste for long hair and black leather jackets so surely we could be friends.

I cooked a few meals for the two of them in our place and a lot of mutual courtship ensued. LX was none too happy to see a new guitarist on the horizon but we didn't want to dump him, he was too valuable a slave and I liked his guitar playing too much for that.

At first we didn't know what we wanted Falco for and in the end we wanted him as a second guitarist in the Kids merely because he was available.

Amel was a wild creature with extra-long black hair who made occasional money hair modelling for Vidal Sassoon. I didn't understand what made her tick. Perhaps if I'd been to Berlin at that time in my life I'd have had a little more respect for her, understood what capable animals European women can be. I was judging her in terms of craven low English bitches I encountered on the London band scene.

Amel would have loved it if the courtship between herself, her man, Jesse and me had ended with me fucking off on a long holiday so she could do a threesome with Jesse and Falco. She brought this Velvet Underground boxed set that I'd never seen before around to our squat and this impressed me. She was a street urchin waif built like a schoolboy, somewhat masculine like a character out of Genet. Tough and fast, an astute player of the game and of the bass.

Amel left the boxed set in our place for months, only removing it in high dudgeon when Texema had broken up, her life had turned upside down, and she knew that she would never get fucked in Subliminal Kids-land.

Later she married a rock star junkie from Australia.

Just like LX showed up in extreme personal circumstances, so Falco appeared at the end of a life-defining saga of sorts. Falco'd been doing good back in Germany in the early Eighties. He played session guitar on an album by a Bonn band which went into the German Indie charts. He had both album and chart with him to prove it. On the back of that success he put Texema together with Amel and things started going good for them. Somewhere on the way to Memphis he ran into a once-legendary English rock'n'roll producer, Ed Hollis.

Hollis was a staff producer at Island Records back in the days of Bob Marley. He produced early English punks The Damned before 'discovering' pub rockers Eddie and The Hot Rods when also-ran bands like them were busy buying leather jackets, going on diets, spiking their hair and converting to punk. Punk, a powerful American dada scene with roots in literature and art, had been thriving in New York since 1971, but didn't hit London until much later, when a uniquely English Music Hall variation on the theme emerged. Hollis co-wrote and produced a single for the Hot Rods—*Do Anything You Wanna Do*—which proved, with its message of football terrace individualism, to be the first big punk hit single in England.

The Hot Rods never had any other hits but Ed Hollis

developed the magic touch which turned yobs into stars. Hollis took a shine to Falco's band.

'Falco, you've got a brilliant presence. Come on over to England, man,' Hollis said. 'I've got a studio in my house where I do all my work now. We can make an album there. I'll bring it around to the labels and see what happens.'

This was the very proposal that every aspirant young German musician wanted to hear, this invitation to go make powerful rock music in London, where Mick had run into Keith on the train and changed the world, blah blah blah.

The way Falco told it, he and Amel high-tailed it to London and moved into Hollis's big country house a few miles out of Brighton. Everything was as Hollis had promised. There was plenty room for them to crash, the studio was fine, and work began on an album.

As the weeks went by things turned to shit. Hollis proved to be a hardcore junkie in the load-out bay, about to be beamed up to a better place, hurtling ninety miles an hour down a dead end street. On Saturdays he'd grimly go into his extraordinary record collection room, grab a few hundred albums, and head for London.

Falco was the chauffeur on these trips—at the wheel of Hollis's vintage white Buick Skylark—because Hollis was banned from driving. First they'd head for the

Record and Tape Exchange in Notting Hill, where he offloaded his vinyl. When he had his money Hollis would instruct Falco to take him to an imposing terraced redbrick in Brixton where he'd pick up a week's supply of scag and, a happy man again, go home to Brighton.

The recording sessions proceeded when Hollis was in the humour. Seven tracks were completed on a beautiful old 24-track analog machine, the perfect equipment for preserving rock'n'roll. The dark brown master tape turned round and round on the big old tape recorder and, even though their lives were surrounded by junkie mayhem, Amel and Falco had the very real consolation of doing good tracks, albeit at a torturously slow pace.

A big day came when everything had been recorded and it was time to do the mixdown, collating the disparate sounds into a whole. Hollis was uptight, running out of gear and anxious to get finished before the weekend, when he'd be heading for London as usual. An all night mixing session accompanied by all night drinking ensued.

Falco was relaxing in the mixing booth, proudly listening to his layers of guitars take shape and form, when a happy Hollis stood up quietly, swayed over the master tape whirring through the machine, and puked all over the tape for two minutes.

The master was destroyed. After that, with less resolve, it was back to square one.

In the weeks that followed the last of Hollis's records went up his arm and he started dismantling the studio and bringing bits and pieces of that up to Notting Hill. The final straw came one day when Falco woke up to find his vintage Fender guitar gone missing. Falco, smart and well educated, got the message. He and Amel collected their next dole cheques, rescued their other guitars and caught the train to London. Two collective squats later, they had their own place in Tulse Hill Estate, and came into our lives.

Falco's family were rich German provincials. I think his old man owned warehouses or real estate or something. While Falco was checking out Aerosmith and the Stones his little brother listened to Bach and Strauss, and grew up to be a classical musician. Falco, like the rest of us, never grew up at all.

It took months to steal Falco, who couldn't abandon his Texema, his Amel, or his ego without a struggle. There was no reason for him to join us other than the sort of blind ambition that wastes the lives of many a green provincial recently arrived in the big city. I don't mean that he behaved stupidly; it's just hard to know what to do when you come to London. In fact you should go back home or somewhere else.

While Falco was playing in Subliminal Kids we read

in the *NME* about the death of Ed Hollis, legendary punk rock record producer.

A red letter day for Subliminal Kids. Miss Amel has waved the white flag and admitted defeat. After Falco broke up Texema she hung on for dear life, wanting the bassist gig in the Kids. LX is nervous enough about Falco without Medusa making things worse. So today she packed up her bags and left Falco, who is all trauma-tised and woman-sore. He did the dishonourable thing by her, and now his penis must pay the awful price. Also she won't be lonely for long, moving in with sicko South African scumbag Paul Woods, whom we call PW in honour of his racist leader, PW Botha.

She says *Oh, it's just a houseshare arrangement* and, for sure, I doubt PW can even get it up.

Jesse introduced Falco to PW when Falco needed a regular dealer. Last week Jesse was looking through a skip and he found some big glass jars containing headless dog foetuses suspended in formaldehyde. The seals on the jars were broken and the foetuses were already degenerating. PW is a member of that sad Temple of Psychic Youth disease so Jesse knew the foetuses would appeal to him. PW could hardly contain himself, offered good cash money, but Jesse did a better deal and swapped hash for the jars.

I kind of objected to Jesse doing the business with the foetuses but I don't know what the fuck I was objecting to. I think I was just bored and needed something to say.

Wasted days and wasted nights

Little story 'bout Jim and Carol or Jack and Diane.

Jim and Carol were an attractive teenage couple I helped get started in London.

Jim couldn't even remember what he looked like himself. He knew he was a pretty street prince—they told him that. He had to get up in the morning to go to the dole office. He was a leopardskin panther lurching away from the lamplight, an animal of the night who never went to bed before the dawn.

His big plan was to fuck with his girlfriend until it was time to head to the dole office. Or handjob himself slowly if the girl didn't show. Or call up to see me and we could do the same thing for one another. Unless the reason she didn't show was because she was entertaining me in a small squat I had for when I couldn't stand the sight of Jesse and for discreet liaisons.

I got off on the fact that I was having relationships with both halves of that lovely couple. They were so decent about their disloyalties, keeping them secret from one another while I kept it secret from everyone.

Jim had to go to the dole office in the morning to report his dole cheque missing and get a replacement issued. Carol got home early, maybe 3AM. Her boss let her off from the Brixton take-away soul food joint. There was no business. 'Yeah, it's nice to get off early,' she said as she relaxed on the couch, 'only I know it means the dump will soon go broke. I just know it.' The boss gave her a doggy bag of OK things to eat, which was fine by Jim who'd been penniless and starving all day. Carol unwrapped pork ribs in a sticky creole sauce and chicken with rice and mushrooms and peas. Carol loaded the food into Jim's little oven and, while the reheating was in progress, he took off her clothes and she took off his. She grabbed his small cock like it was a door handle and gave it a perfunctory tug. He began to swell and rise up at the root.

'Later,' she whispered gently as she let him go, 'because we must eat first.'

While they were eating and telling each other funny stories, naked with the central heating system turned up full blast to fend off the winter chill outside, they played a Suicidal Tendencies album. He liked grungey guitar music, she was more into smoochy soul/jazz sounds. He didn't trust that kind of champagne music but the two of them were movie buffs, met at a late night Clint Eastwood triple bill at the Ritzy. Jim chatted her up professionally before dragging her back to his Coldharbour Lane squat where they talked and fucked and talked and fucked. 'Clint is just old school now,' Jim said to her, 'like the way John Wayne was for our parents.'

Those two kids were so poor and scared of the world that excellent things in their lives seemed like ordinary shit to them. They were smart and knew that later, when they were much older, they'd look back on those Brixton days with fond remembrance while recalling that it was a shit time in their lives.

After eating she spent a while massaging him and licking him and kissing him until he got long, tight and strong the way he liked it, when the skin hurt. Then he sodomised her on the double mattress on the floor as a mix tape of Dinosaur Jr and Nirvana played on their rickety plastic stereo. When they finished they were torn and sore.

Carol was a local Brixton girl. Jim came to London because he'd read about it in the papers, because his mother was English, because he had an exaggerated notion of what sort of city it might be. Like a lot of Americans with dashed expectations he stayed longer than he'd intended and, in reality, liked it there. Brixton was the free zone he'd sought all his life, where he could disappear into the stew.

'That postman hates us,' he said, washing his knob in the bathroom sink. 'I'm sure he threw away my dole because that's the second time it's happened now. If it happens a third time I'll be suspended and totally fucked. I don't know how much longer I can take this life, man, if I could live in a real house and have a real life I'd get some proper money.'

'Yeah,' she said, wrapping a stained bedsheet around her body, 'it's nice and stuff to be with you here but...it won't go on forever, will it?'

He was not a stupid boy and her words sent a cold chill right through him. She was the sensible one. He was a lovable fool. So the night went.

The welfare building was a beautiful place, at one time the only dole office in South London, entirely responsible for the fact that blacks settled in Brixton in the first place. Five hundred black men arrived in town in 1948 on their personal nigger Mayflower, an old merchant ship called the Empire Windrush. Lured by offers of labouring work, those wise men settled where you could get the dole, and they never budged.

It proved a biting cold morning; two young Arabs argued bitterly in Arabic in front the dole office, venting their frustrations with arms extended towards the sky, their guttural voices suggesting that their conversation concerned some vital obscure aspect of Islamic law. Jim loved the fact that Brixton was full of the races, he loved to be with black girls because peoples didn't mix with ease in California.

Three black guys dressed in uniform black denim jeans and black bomber jackets were right in front of him in the queue. Senior niggers, loud and aggressive, built up from pumping iron, Jim knew them as asshole bouncers/dealers from The Fridge. They didn't like the look of Jim either in his frayed Levis, threadbare Converse All Stars and embroidered black silk shirt. His neck was all purple and yellow from lovebites, his broken nose gave him a patrician look, and no amount of London gloom could disguise his well heeled California breeding. The niggers saw he was a squatter, a white middle class boy slumming it up in their negritude.

In front of the niggers stood a black granny trying to collect her husband's money because the old guy was too sick to come in himself. The staff were sort of helpful; she'd have to go to another office two miles away where they could deal with her situation, she just wasn't entitled to collect his money. The welfare staff were all black, their parents probably the same age as the old woman they were dealing with.

At the next hatch to Jim a grossly fat 'Client Advisor' was in charge, all sexed up by the beautiful black dole claimant he was dealing with. He said he'd seen her the previous Saturday at a Streatham nightclub called Porkchoppers. Jim studied her pert little ass until his own turn came to be dealt with by an advisor. She believed him when he said his dole'd disappeared, which made life easier for him. The dole was the best scam in town. His entire dole claim was phony, built up from a British National Insurance Card he'd bought in his last squat.

She said he'd get a replacement cheque if he came back two hours later. High on his fraud, he went to a Brixton Market greasy spoon behind the welfare building to while away the waiting time. He bought a comic along the way, and settled into a cup of strong black tea in the steamy heat of the cafe. Tea was another thing he liked about England—he'd picked up a taste for it from his mother.

Right away he noticed a guy at the next table watching him, a good looking white youth about his own age and height with a fresh lime green mohawk haircut, well tanned skin, a taut muscled physique; Jim's brother squatter. Jim liked the access to fags he got in London. Macho punk fags kept to themselves in California where they were into their tiny exclusive S&M hardcore music skate scenes. Jim didn't fancy going that way. The mohawk nodded to him and Jim beckoned him over to the table.

'Hi, I'm Jim,' he said, standing to shake the punk's hand.

'Yeah? I'm Toby,' said the kid grinning, 'and you're American.'

'Yes and no. The American abroad,' Jim kind of

whispered as he sat back down again.

'Huh! An American abroad then. That makes *all* the difference,' Toby said as he sat opposite Jim, laughing a horny laugh. 'A big difference. Course I've never been in America so that's the only kind of American I've ever met.'

The punk hungrily absorbed Jim's face as he leaned back to rescue his cigarettes from the table behind. As he stretched right back his crotch jutted into the air in front of Jim.

'I've been watching you a lot Jimbo. I used to live across the way from you on Tulse Hill. You ever seen me?'

'No,' Jim said, 'never noticed you, but don't take it personally.'

'I fucking don't take nothing personally,' Toby said genially. 'You've never seen me. I ain't the personal type, but you! You're the loose type. I see you with that beautiful black girl and I see you with that older dude, the longhaired one who lives with the sexy Irish singer. So we must...'

'Yeah, yeah, we must. You got a phone?'

'No. Now I'm in this fucking huge squat on Railton Road and Telecom'd never put a phone into the place.'

'I got a phone,' Jim said all hot. 'I've got a phone. I'll give you the number and let's meet for a drink sometime.'

'Sometime in the next forty-eight hours, fucker, *you*'ll

be doin' the drinkin'.'

'OK.' Jim's tone was blank and neutral. 'I don't think I'll be in London much longer so if you want me, come get me. How'd you know about me and Kim?'

'I'll tell you when I've done ya. Give me your number, I'll give you my address.'

When Jim got his cheque he cashed it quickly, bought supplies in the market, and went back to his home. A letter from Carol waited for him on their double mattress, announcing that the friendship was over, that she was going to Paris with an old boyfriend, or some improbable other bullshit. Or maybe Carol meant it when she wrote the letter. Jim didn't care too much, she was a woman who intrigued him, She had her own business to do.

Jim studied an events poster for the Ritzy pinned to the noticeboard in the kitchen and saw that they had a Seventies late night double bill of Performance and Girl On A Motorcycle on Saturday night. Jim loved those old Stones' babes, that was the type of white girl he really liked. You got in cheap to the Ritzy with a dole card.

He felt like sleeping, yet he wanted to come before he slept. He poked frantically in his hip pocket and found the scrap of paper with Toby's address. He slapped on a mix tape of Sepultura, Slayer, the Stones and Anthrax.

He ran a bath, took off all his clothes, and spent an hour in the hot water soaking.

Out on the street while it got dark he wandered towards Railton Road. He didn't need the address to spot the decrepit overgrown garden, the Jamaican flag flying from the roof, the Acid House blasting from the front room, or the rainbow-painted windows of the house where Toby lived. He banged on the front door for ten minutes before a girl in a filthy t-shirt and jeans answered. She welcomed him in and pointed out Toby's room on the second floor.

I know what happen to Carol, Toby and Jim in those days because Carol and Jim told me all about it the following day; he by way of pillow talk, she by way of telephone conversation. Their stories tallied, they lied to one another but not to me.

Nigel

That stupid Japanese cow, Noko, who came to all the gigs by the Kids back then, was on the phone to me last night.

Her problem is Nigel's cymbals, which she bought at the Record and Tape Exchange under instructions from Jesse after Nigel sold them there towards the end. Jesse thought at the time that Nigel would be coming back to us, that he might need them again. They still have his blood all over them, black encrusted lumps on the smooth surfaces. The day he took them away from us he lost a lot of blood. I'd love to run my fingers over the blood sometime because that's the only part of Nigel that's left. Now she is screaming like a pig on the phone. What's the problem? She has the cymbals in their original Cult flight cases under her bed.

And the cymbals are moving around the floor!!

So I just say to her: 'Noko, here's what you do. Just tell Nigel to stop moving them around and it'll be OK.'

That only makes her scream the more.

How'd she get my phone number? From Jesse? He says he's not in touch with her anymore. I must change it.

LX has this connection on Memphisto, a dire Norwich Goth band who've a big following up North who've just signed a deal, who've got, lots of groupies with names like Astral and Stargazer and Moonchild. More accurate appellations might be Blow Job Queen or Cunt Central.

Memphisto's male fans are all sturdy collegiate longhairs with big testicles, busy smoking dope in the dormitories of various provincial universities, listening to new Van Morrison or old Led Zeppelin albums. The sperm from those big testicles swims freely up the valleys of the Moonchilds and Stargazers during cosmic rituals enacted in the backs of transit vans all over yokel England.

The menfolk roll joints, the girls cook crappy vegetarian gunk.

Somebody in the Memphisto organisation made the ultimate sacrifice to get this record deal, for no English rock band has ever been signed to ADLAI Records without the notorious child molester, Ed Freeman, Head of A&R at ADLAI, getting his hands down the trousers of at least one band member. Freeman was a minor alternative movie star before he went bald, appearing in indie fag flicks and directing 'the first punk rock movie'. Whatever that means. He gets his knob sucked nightly and by pretty nice looking boys too.

Band members are such hopeless losers. Every time I see him I think *Hey, Ed, maybe you should set yourself a challenge sometime and try to rape somebody who isn't weak, gullible, ambitious and a whore?*

To celebrate their historic signing to ADLAI, whose roster includes actual American guitar-band superstars, Memphisto get to play the Marquee and they ask us if the Kids want the support slot and of course we do. Our drummer is in a state of ecstasy about playing the hallowed stage of the Marquee where every so-fucking-what you've ever heard of, like Jimmy Page or Eric Clapton, has cut his chops.

Only the *real* Marquee where the Stones conquered

London and changed the world is in the next street and *this* Marquee used to be a cinema until about twelve months ago when Rod Stewart's manager bought the name and moved it to a more tourist-friendly spot. We're still on for it because the Kids can always tell the Japs and the Yanks that we did the Marquee and changed the world. Also we need someplace impressive to hold a meeting.

Falco says he met this Nigel character in the George Robey who was the drummer in The Cult, not some stand-in but the founder-drummer who came out of The Death Cult, helped form The Cult, played on *She Sells Sanctuary*, the real thing. It seems deeply improbable to me that Falco has been socialising so high up rock's totem pole in a lowlife dive like the George Robey, but Falco swears he has his facts right and that if we put this Nigel dude down on the Marquee guest list he'll come along to meet with us. He's not playing with anyone and wants to get into a band.

Backstage on the Big Night I'm watching Memphisto take their showers while Ed Freeman is sniffing **around** like a dog. He is paying too much attention to LX and I'm thinking *Go for it, LX, get us a deal while giving true expression to your femininity at the same time.*

Falco walks in and says the guy from The Cult is outside and do we want to meet with him. So yeah, and soon Mr Cult joins us in a black suit, collar and tie, hair cut short. I don't know what he looks like but he sure don't seem like a King of Cock Rock. He's handsome in an old-world way, his manners are impeccable, he looks like he has money. He shakes hands with everybody and says how pleased he is to meet us, that he'll come back after the set. Then he disappears and keeps his promise by returning the second Jesse strides offstage.

The gig goes well. Our drummer is a New Zealand moron in love with his hairy sister who thinks, Jesse being Irish, that he's in Thin Lizzy. He used to be in a Lizzy cover band down under and is all fucked up tonight because he smells the presence of The Cult guy. He'll be fired anyway—I have it in for him. On the way back from a gig in Manchester last week it was his turn to drive and he refused to make a piss-stop for a hundred miles even though everybody wanted a piss.

LX is on his best behaviour because Memphisto are his pals, he used to be in a band with some of them or something. He is wearing a pink and cream striped YSL jacket that Noko gave Jesse and which Jesse gave him. Since the drummer is shit and the guitarist is barely competent, everything rests on Jesse's shoulders. He has star written all over him, as usual, and his songs win the day. There are about two hundred people lurking around the edges of the auditorium, with maybe fifty more gathered closer to the stage. Noko is in the house with her three pals, shooting off roll after roll of film and wiping perspiration from her face.

I love it, the band hate it, but that is normal. The band always hate the good gigs and think the bad ones are successful.

There is something about this Cult guy I like a lot even though it's only small talk and a toke with him backstage. He says: 'Congratulations, chaps. I thought it was powerful. I really loved those songs Jesse. I'll phone tomorrow to arrange a jam if you'd like.' Maybe he will, maybe he won't. Hopefully he'll bring the summer with him if he comes.

Algeciras

Lisa rings me. I'm pleased by her interruption because I sometimes get lonely when I'm in Algeciras—unlike Berlin, which is allnight and social. I haven't seen her since she and Screw left Brixton but she keeps in touch about once a year on the phone. She has a business in San Francisco.

Lisa sounds like she's twenty again, bubbling with enthusiasm.

'You'd never guess who I fucking saw tonight?' she says in a North Dublin accent that'd strip paint.

'Who'd you see, Lisa? Who'd you see?' I mock her.

'Angela fucking Davis!' Lisa says. 'I was doing a picket on a concert at Berkeley and Angela Davis walks up to me and takes one of the fucking leaflets!'

'Wow!' I say. I *am* impressed. 'The sweet black angel!'

'The very one.' Lisa laughs. 'So of course I told her about the factory and the Angela Davis Industrial Estate. She just laughed.'

'What'd she look like? Does she still look good?' I ask.

'She looks fucking great!' Lisa reports.

We talk for an hour. She pays for half of it and then I call her back. It's like that fucking awful Christmas song about I met my old lover in a grocery store.

After the phonecall, I head out to an allnight coffee shop and sit under a canopy in the open air.

Disaffected youths on motorcycles whir all around me, defining the Mediterranean style of the town. Last night, listening to the radio while lying in bed, I heard about the leader of the paramilitary wing of a leftist youth movement who was arrested in Malaga and charged with sedition. Today the local motorcycle kids react by rioting in the streets.

The last thing I said to Lisa was: 'You lucky bitch! I'd fucking love to meet Angela Davis.'

This is a remix

I'm just out there gazing over the wasteland that exists between my high-rise and the one opposite when my eyes stray up to LX's bohemian love pad, the splendid spot we found the Cornwall boy so he can be in peace.

I ask myself *Does LX ever get to sustain any girlfriend-style arrangements?* There are occasional casual pickups that I know of but those are innocent out-of-town girls who don't know what they're letting themselves in for. Women find him shifty and low rent, I know they do, they've told me so. One girl he fucked...I don't think I even want to go into that. I'm feeling too good.

What do my eyes behold while I'm daydreaming about him but, not for the first time, LX in deep deep trouble.

LX is walking purposefully towards the lift. He is pale and his lips are pursed. There are three miserable looking middle aged niggers walking behind him. I didn't know LX knew any niggers! LX summons the lift while the men, looking grim and pissed off, gather in a circle around him. The lift comes and they all get in, LX first. I assume they're going to the ground floor so I concentrate my attention on where the lift meets the ground. About a minute later they get out and the niggers march to a waiting dark blue Toyota estate with the engine running and a woman driver behind the wheel. LX stands there limply just looking at them as if they've just taken turns in diddling him. They get inside, the driver revs up the engine and they head off towards the exit.

When the noise of the engine dies off I shout 'Yo LX!' to our guitar hero and he looks up at me in shock, all shifty that I've been watching him. 'Oh, hi!' he shouts in his elitist hippy Cornwall accent, very much unsure of himself either because of what went down in his flat or because I've been watching him in action or because he got no sleep last night or he needs to borrow a tenner from me or, when it comes right down to it with LX, who knows the fuck what's going on inside his head?

Anyway he walks over to my lift and he joins me within the minute.

'Hi man, what gives with you and the homies?' I ask, getting right to the point.

'What homies?' asks LX and you got to hand it to LX for audacity and grace under pressure.

'Man, the fucking homies who came out of your flat and who looked like they were fucking about to execute you,' I say, laughing despite myself.

'Ah, yes,' he says, pausing for effect and to think up an excuse, 'they were just looking for a previous tenant and I was coming over to see you anyway because I got you a little present.'

And indeed he does have a little present for me, a

baggy of cocaine which has the desired effect of distracting my attention from the niggers and forcing me to get my priorities in order. We walk into my hallway where LX stands still, looking at me, his head bowed like a puppy dog wanting affection from his owner. I rub my right hand through his very long dyed blonde hair; that's all the affection he's going to get.

'Any news?' he asks.

'Nah.' I put some coke onto an Eric B & Rakim CD box and chop out two lines with a Telecom chargecard. 'I did have Noko on the phone earlier. She woke me up.'

'Oh, her,' says LX. He has a healthy disregard for Noko. 'What did she want? An English lesson?'

'No, I don't think so.' I laugh. 'She has much bigger problems right now...to do with her inheritance.'

'I thought she had more money than she knows what to do with,' LX snorts derisively.

'Yeah she has, but you know the way she has this brother that she's always saying is a fag?' I walk into the kitchen and find a shortened McDonalds straw. I hand it to him first. He got the shit. Where? How?

'She showed me a photograph of him.' LX snorts his line like a man.

'Well, fag or no fag,' it's my turn now, 'he's getting married and his would-be wife is up the pole so...'

'So now there's a son and heir to the real estate fortune.' LX can always follow the thread when it involves money.

'Perhaps. Perhaps.' I'm lunging at the baggie again, pouring some more onto the CD box. 'She was fucking cursing and swearing about the brother anyway, how he hates her parents, how he wears make-up, how his wife -to-be is evil...the bitch won't look after Noko's mother who has a heart problem...the brother has this best friend who likes The Bee Gees...But fuck her, you know? I told her to call later when Jesse's back. She's his predicament.'

'Those fucking Japs, they'd eat their own,' LX says. 'Look what they did to poor David Bowie.'

Mansion on the hill

The downstairs crack dealer was a whole other kettle of fish.

He was Jay, a genial middle-aged Rasta with a six year old daughter to support. Jay was born in Montego Bay but his folks moved to London when he was just five. I didn't get into nigger flats too often but I visited Jay pretty regularly, enjoying his booming system dub reggae and poking through his sitting room full of stolen goods...CD players, dodgy credit cards, passports, crates of vodka, tumble dryers and microwaves still in their boxes.

'Anything at all, man, anything at all,' Jay promised whenever I departed having bought something small like a bottle of whiskey. I loved his funky attitude.

Bunk, the upstairs dealer, was just a boy but Jay was the boss man on our estate. All the urchins, black or white, looked up to him and when they had hot stuff to flog they'd go see Jay first. He had first refusal on everything, mainly because he paid the right price. I know this because he regularly fenced stuff for Nigel and occasionally for Jesse or me. LX's relationship with him was a whole other more complex thing; our guitar hero was typically discreet in his dealings with Jay.

Jay sold us crack when we were in that mood but buying ganja from him was always a big disaster. Nigel, who was maybe a little bit racist but afraid to show it in front of white niggers like Jesse, liked Jay and sometimes holed up with him when he was in his cups, but advised, 'Never buy hash from a street nigger.' In Jay's case he had a point because it was always rock-hard slate adulterated with henna and amphetamine and sedative: street hash. Jay made his living as a major dealer down the Front Line.

Jay was very much a man alone. It was him, his kid and his Alsatian against the world. He had a girlfriend that I saw coming and going but never met, a conservatively dressed older woman who, improbable as it seemed, was a lawyer. He was every bit as much outside of society as me and LX and Jesse were. Unlike us, however, he had a childish attitude to the real world, saw it as a funny white place out there in the distance.

Sometimes he was under pressure and a surly old bear who'd indulge in one of those routines that niggers *will* try on with the white man—he'd hit us for money. The huge across-the-great-divide we-are-the-world racial harmony that existed between the lot of us would taper off to be replaced by somewhat comic efforts at intimidation. But we were neighbours, sometimes it got down to borrowing tea-bags or a quid from one another, so it was tough for him to turn on the nigger tricks that worked so good with English white boys.

Most nights, when LX drove me down to the factory, Jay would appear out of nowhere, from the badly lit corridors of Ralston House, and hit us for a lift to the Front Line. I noted during these trips the subtle mutualities that existed between LX and Jay, which I assumed had something to do with Jay's invaluable roles as fence and dealer. LX was free to do whatever he wanted in his own time, to think his own little thoughts, to go out and play with his own friends, so long as he was our abject slave when we needed him.

Other times I noted mysterious circumstances which made the mind, or what was left of it, boggle.

One summer day, right out of the blue, LX triumphantly announced that he'd got us a second canary yellow Volvo, identical in every way to our car. LX's deeply improbable story was that he'd been down in the supermarket car park when he was approached by a street nigger he'd never met before but whom he vaguely remembered seeing at Jay's place once or twice. The nigger had seen our Volvo and wanted to know if LX wanted to buy a second one for parts.

LX said he did want the second car but that he had no money. The man said to LX that he could have it anyway, pay for it when he was in funds. Such community-oriented generosity! So it was arranged that LX could pick it up the next evening. We helped him get it to the yard in front of the factory and there, the following weekend, we stripped it for parts. We left the yellow shell right there; as far as I was concerned it was a kind of fluxus thing, sprouting weeds and gathering rust.

The weeks passed, and I quite forgot about the origins of the second Volvo. The spare parts proved invaluable, reviving our flagging jalopy.

One blistering summer day me and LX were heading south towards Brixton listening to The Ramones and The Beach Boys.

We were caught in a traffic jam close to the Oval when this homie in the car next to us starts gesticulating and shouting. He'd been shouting and roaring for quite some time when I noted his high anxiety. He was in the throes of vast petulance when I finally paid attention to him. His girlfriend was a Janet Jackson lookalike and she stared respectfully at her man while he emoted. Oddly enough, LX appeared to be blissfully unaware of it all.

'That asshole in the next car is really pissed off with us,' I said eventually because this was a dangerous looking customer, a gangster.

'Oh really,' said LX laughing nervously, 'perhaps he doesn't like the music.'

'He can't hear the fucking music,' I said. 'Are you doing anything wrong with the driving?'

'Actually, hmm, that's the fellow who gave us the second Volvo,' he said, coughing nervously as if he were clearing a frog in his throat.

'What the fuck does he want then?' I asked. Our buddy looked dangerous like he was about to explode.

'Maybe he wants some money for his car,' said LX. 'Last time I saw him he made some mention of wanting money for it.'

'I thought you said that you explained to him that you didn't have any money to pay for the fucking thing,' I shouted.

'Oh, yes,' said a flustered LX. 'Only subsequently… though…he has mentioned money.'

'*Subsequently?*'

Silence.

I was about to suggest that if it was such a big deal I could toss a few quid his way when the gangster got out of his car in the middle of the traffic jam and strode in our direction. As he marched his chick began to glare at LX, supporting her man as only a Janet Jackson can.

When he reached us he nodded amicably enough to me and went round to the driver's side where LX was turning green.

'Where's my money, my man?' he said all tough-but-amicable, no small talk.

'I just don't have any,' said LX sheepishly.

'Well, you should have thought about that before, then, shouldn't you?' said the homie, now sounding mean and evil.

It was turning into a real Superfly situation. LX's man got more and more bothered as LX calmly delivered superbly vague responses to direct and unequivocal questions. It had nothing to do with the Volvo (God knows what part the spare car had actually played in the great scheme of things) and everything to do with something illegal.

Just when I thought Superfly was going to pull a gun or be dramatic like that the traffic miraculously unclogged and began to move, and Janet Jackson called him back to the car.

As he departed he stared maliciously at LX who turned up the music, as if the sheer volume would drive the nigger away: as if LX was most anxious to hear the track then playing, *I Get Around* by The Beach Boys. Once the traffic moved it moved fast. Soon we lost sight of LX's pal.

'What the fuck was all that about?' I asked as we picked up speed, sniffing Brixton in the distance.

'Oh, really, who can tell with these people?' said LX, sighing theatrically.

'*These people?*' I stared at him in awe.

'Some of these characters are addicted to crack and have smoked themselves psycho.' Like he was writing the entry on crack for the Encyclopedia Britannica, like neither of us had ever used crack Cocaine. He said little else on the way home, worrying about something he had no intention of telling me about.

These little larks were fun and games for me but LX was obviously travelling through the dark primitive underbelly of South London. The shell of our second Volvo, worthless and useless, disappeared from in front of the factory two weeks later. I spotted its absence one night when LX was dropping me there.

'The fucking car has gone,' I said in amazement.

'So it has!' said LX in his finest Home Counties accent, feigning surprise and dismay.

Ghost on the highway

I was hunting for niggers down in the dark.
Then all of a sudden I had a better thought.
Gonna buy me a graveyard of my own
And kill everyone who ever done me wrong.
—The Gun Club

It's a long long way down rock'n'roll. Your name gets hot and your heart grows cold.

Everything is irreversible.

The Gun Club had gone a long way down by the time I met up with them. Nigel was the connection. Nigel, six foot tall, riding high in the saddle, python, rattler, baby snake, always broke and mostly bombed, was still a star drummer and quite employable. He'd done a lot of session work with The Gun Club and with their charismatic leader, Jeffrey Lee Pierce. Japs were the connection between those two dead men: Nigel was married to Kaz, a beautiful pencil-thin Japanese woman, while Jeffrey lived with Kaz's best pal, a woman called Romi Mori, bass player to The Gun Club.

The Gun Club had been a very big post-punk deal, rejecting punk's arrogance as punk had rejected the self-importance of the hippies. They even got signed to the huge Elektra Records and, another time, Chris Stein from Blondie took them under his wing, giving them a touch of that magic Blondie thing. The music was swamp rock out of country blues, whiskey, drugs, LA, and Jeffrey Lee's bizarre personality. The Gun Club belonged to a wave of LA groups including punk/hardcore maestros X and the eventually huge Red Hot Chilli Peppers. Jeffrey Lee was hard to deal with and never kept a line-up going too long.

The Gun Club inevitably ran out of emotional steam and America rejected Jeffrey Lee. A shattered man, he washed up in London where he recorded his alarming and very brilliant solo album, *Wildweed*, which was never out of the English Indie charts at one time during the late Eighties. *Wildweed* remains a brilliant American testament right up there with Faulkner, F. Scott Fitzgerald and William Burroughs. The sepia cover shows Jeffrey Lee wielding a shotgun against a blasted-heath backdrop. On it he looks like a blonde handsome American icon, the sort of guy he wanted to be but never was. Nigel played on the album, one of the reasons we took him into Subliminal Kids.

When I knew Jeffrey Lee he had a lot of problems to do with his sex life, his body and interacting with other humans. He'd fought with everybody, made life difficult for those who loved him, written powerful songs of isolation and desolation. He was still pally with contemporaries like Nick Cave but his commercial following had dwindled down to Gun Club completists who thronged to mediocre but lucrative gigs across Europe.

Jeffrey Lee admired Brando and always had had a weight problem, but by the time I knew him he was fatter even than Brando in Apocalypse Now, living under a similarly paranoid siege mentality. He rarely hit the streets, but cowered in his Shepherd's Bush lair like a wounded bear, misanthropic and heartbroken, Napoleon on Elba watching his world collapse and waiting for his people to summon him back home. When Jesse first formed Subliminal Kids he modelled the band's sound on The Gun Club. Now that Nigel had introduced us to the big guy, Jesse wanted Jeffrey Lee to produce an album for him.

One year our lives intimately touched the lives of Jeffrey Lee and his band. Nigel believed The Gun Club were a shit group lead by a talentless and pompous bozo. His only interest was in the well-paid session gigs he occasionally got with them. Jeffrey, for his part, was scared and intimidated by Nigel who embodied the essence of the romantic rock sedition at the very heart of Jeffrey Lee's persona—but far away from the reality of Jeffrey's day to day life. Like other American musicians on that professionally weird scene, Jeffrey Lee had a puritanical streak a mile wide, born out of the famously gross excesses of his salad days and the ensuing self-denial. He thought of Nigel as a sinner, and of me as a far more grievous angel.

In the glory days of The Gun Club he'd swallowed

every pill put in front of him, grown addicted to heroin and been the playboy of the western world. As a result he had no liver worth talking about; he was under continual and strict medical supervision. He lived in England because, back home, he couldn't afford the health care he needed and in England they still had a National Health Service of sorts, from which he got his medication for free. It was all chicken breasts, steamed vegetables and Diet Coke for Ramblin' Jeffrey Lee. Diet Coke or Death.

Money came from mercenary forays onto the European club circuit with a pick-up Gun Club—which usually included Nigel—fronted by Romi and Jeffrey. There was no other regular money. Sometimes amps and guitars were sold either to the Record and Tape Exchange or to friends like Jesse, who ended up with the amp Jeffrey had used to make *Wildweed*. Album advances and residual royalties allowed him to splash out from time to time, indulging his passion for foreign travel. A new Gun Club album was always good for some sales and he was a canny negotiator when it came to advance-hunting. In tight circumstances Jeffrey Lee was forced to be prolific and, as a result, created difficult, kaleidoscopic visions of exile.

Jeffrey and Romi shared a cramped ground floor flat on a leafy backstreet between Shepherd's Bush and Notting Hill with two other Japanese women, buddies of Romi's and of Nigel's wife Kaz. It all went around in circles.

Their living room, where Jeffrey always hung out, was dominated by a TV screen big enough for a lounge bar on which Jeffrey Lee watched four or five satellite channels. Mostly it was tuned in to MTV. When I'd call to see him, this paragon of hardcore American credibility, I might well be treated to a two hour special on land reclamation in Egypt, three in a row from Bruce Springsteen or an hour long in-concert from Mötley Crüe.

Jeffrey was caught up on the blues, every guitarist's failing. Most conversations with him—monologues really—took place as he sat on the edge of a stool, strumming his guitar: 'We played *Heroin* in Belgium because we've run out of fast songs...My favourite record right now is the new Prince album...This is great stuff, y'know, better than us. I mean we're not The Beatles, man, who cares? We're just The Gun Club. I hate America, I hate everywhere. I know where my dream home is, between Romi's legs. I wanna play sax more. That's more to do with Charlie Parker than Coltrane and a love of noise...My favourite colour is angry red, screaming red.'

Somewhere along the line he stopped being a precocious boy genius having his picture taken with Debbie Harry, and turned into a middle aged crazy. He slept all day and stayed awake all night listening to blues records, learning how to imitate Jimi's guitar licks, pointing out to his captive Jap audience how ZZ Top had ripped off such and such a riff from an obscure 1938 recording by Blind Lemon Jefferson.

Most days he didn't shave, walked the world in a grey tracksuit, drank Diet Coke and talked about his health. When he talked to me it was often about Jimi Hendrix, his conversation implying that Hendrix was some obscure genius that he had unique insights on. He somehow imagined that we shared a passion for Hendrix whereas, in reality, I can't stand that music. When it comes to that kind of guitar solo, I don't want to know.

Jeffrey's life was a cut-price operation. To save money and time when Nigel was drumming with both bands, Subliminal Kids shared an Elephant & Castle rehearsal room with him. Nigel'd do a session with the Kids, rest for an hour, and then do The Gun Club. Powerfully built, with a smart kid mentality, Preston loved drumming. Towards the end of each Kids' rehearsal, when Jeffrey was due to show up, Nigel would start moaning humorously: 'Oh my God! This is fun but I've got to do six more hours now with Jeffrey and he'll be doing those awful fucking songs in his raincoat! Course he pays me, not like you cunts.'

At first Jeffrey was very enthusiastic about producing Jesse. A lot of his visits to the factory concerned that project. He was legitimately busy a lot of the time, often away touring Europe to pay the rent.

Unexpectedly, an album advance arrived, so he planned a big holiday in Vietnam, preparing for his trip with military precision. He was profoundly supportive of the Vietnamese people, having enjoyed an American adolescence at the end of the Vietnam War. Now he was all busy reading travel writing and Vietnamese literature, and consulting maps. First he'd visit India, spend ten days there before doing a month in Vietnam. After Vietnam he planned to go to Japan, where Romi would be visiting her family. Upon his return from Japan, his batteries recharged, he promised that work would begin on the Subliminal Kids project in earnest.

We had a few doubts about our new friend when we caught The Gun Club at a rare English gig in a horrible South London dive called The Venue. Kid Congo Powers, the sexy Latino androgyne who played weird guitar with the band, flew in from LA for that tour.

Kid Congo was vital for high-profile Gun Club outings because the "kids" identified with him. With his rockabilly amphetamine image, his dangerous look, his thin beautiful body, Kid Congo was the latin lover rockist vision that Gun Club fans aspired towards. The loose collection of session players plus Romi that Jeffrey called The Gun Club was fine in the European boondocks but he needed the Kid for English-speaking territories. The Kid was a bigger star than Jeffrey, as his hugely commercial alternative careers with Nick Cave and The Cramps proved.

The Venue gig was a merciless night attended by six hundred ageing and balding male rockists, all decked out in leather and black: hardcore fanatical fans. Backstage the atmosphere was funereal before the band went on. Neither myself nor Jesse had seen The Gun Club live and two hours later I knew why they kept themselves strictly out of town. What they played that night wasn't music— more self-centred exorcism. We dutifully trooped backstage afterwards to mouth insincere nice things and congratulations.

In an inner sanctum Jeffrey held court, Apocalypse Now-style, surrounded by loyal retainers, i.e. the Japs. Kid Congo maintained a discreet distance.

Jesse was interested in getting a sniff of Kid Congo so he stuck it out. I walked back to the hall. Most of the guys at the bar were my contemporaries or younger than me, caught up in a rock vision I rejected. Indeed, that gig played a major part in my rejection of the whole concept of song-based music. I was thinking about sneaking away and catching a taxi home when I noticed a genuine Gun Club superstar heading towards the aftershow.

She was Patricia Morrison, bass player before Romi. She'd quit the band amid loads of publicity to join chart-topping Goth stars The Sisters of Mercy, a naff crew catering to stupid fucked-up Goth fans. Phenomenally popular at that time, they filled real big halls, used big-shot producers, were going to the top. Morrison, a glamorous tall woman with spiky black hair, dressed from head to toe in black leather, stood out in any crowd. Her move from the middle-range popularity of The Gun Club to the Top of the Pops *chic* of The Sisters threw Jeffrey's plight into sharp relief. Amid the bleak monochrome milieu of The Gun Club, she was the glitziest possible creature, a counterculture sex symbol.

Naturally, I followed her backstage. It would be interesting to see how Jeffrey, well on the way to being a has-been, and Romi, Morrison's alluring enough replacement, handled her arrival.

By the time I got to the dressing room about two minutes later, the shit had hit the fan. In the master's chamber the three people who'd made The Gun Club famous—Jeffrey Lee, Kid Congo, and Patricia Morrison—huddled in profound discomfort surrounded by Romi, the other Japs, Jesse, Nigel and Nigel's wife Kaz. The atmosphere was like the inside of a microwave: psychic darts going off in every direction. Jeffrey Lee had malevolently launched into a fantastic monologue about an undignified sexual encounter involving Morrison, a table and a prominent member of yet another superstar Goth band.

The Goth movement was a weird beast. Most of the

boys dyed their spiked hair jet-black, wore heavy black eyeliner, dressed in tight black trousers that made their genitals protrude, and were often to be seen in long black raincoats or black leather overcoats, even at the height of the Summer. Goth men looked and behaved like effeminate homosexuals. Ninety-five per cent of them had girlfriends—big bossy girls wearing the exact same clothes, often hugely fat or abnormally tall, with brusque deep voices. The girls looked for all the world like bull dykes or fag hags and the men, wherever their contradictory sexuality was leading them, were no match for them. Jeffrey Lee was the Godfather of Goth. He looked more like the fat girls than the faggy boys, but this strange movement that he spawned enjoyed commercial success he only dreamed of.

I didn't want to hear more of Jeffrey's story about Morrison so I quit the dressing room. Five minutes later roaring and shouting erupted and Patricia Morrison, rock diva, stormed out on the verge of tears. She wryly shook her head in disbelief, mumbling: 'Jeffrey Lee!' as she disappeared into the night.

I didn't see anything of them after that gig or for months afterwards. Jeffrey went off on his South East Asian holiday. Then one night in the middle of the night I got a phonecall from Romi, pretending that it was only yesterday that we last spoke.

'Did you hear about Jeffrey?' Romi asked rhetorically. I heard that question three times over four years, and the saga that followed the question was, each time, grim and epic.

'Nah,' I said, 'I was expecting to hear from you guys sometime though.'

'I'm finished with him after that trip,' she said. 'It was too much.'

Jeffrey Lee and Romi were in India two days when he bought a bottle of Evian from a street vendor. The seemingly sealed bottle contained ordinary tap water, putrid with every germ and bug known to man. Within four hours Jeffrey, whose life hung by a thread at the best of times, was in intensive care at death's door. He stayed in a coma for three days, remained in the hospital for four weeks and then, with a stubbornness which was one of his good sides, travelled on to Vietnam. Romi nursed him in his Indian hospital but when he went to Vietnam, she went home to Tokyo.

For fourteen days he made a magnificent progression through the country of his dreams. His father had been a Kennedy-era Democrat union organiser and Jeffrey had a sometimes leftist perspective. Things turned sour when he headed north to the onetime strongholds of the Viet Cong. The people up there still felt bad about the fact that Jeffrey's people had waged genocide against them. They called him 'Fat Yankee' and he got stoned (with rocks) several times.

Jeffrey Lee marched, good times and bad times, remorselessly north oblivious to hostility. Eventually he was attacked by four anti-imperialist juvenile delinquents who stole his money, kicked the shit out of him, broke a lot of bones, and knifed him three times. They left him for dead but he was far from dead. Back in a Third World hospital again, he began his fight back to health.

He phoned Romi and she flew, with funds, from Tokyo to Hanoi to do more nursing. Three weeks later she took him to her family's home in Japan for a month's hand-holding before returning dispirited to London.

'Poor Jeffrey,' I commented, wanting to broach the pathetic nature of his situation. 'I guess he needs somebody to look after him. His health is so bad.'

'Yes,' she said. 'It is really terrible living with him. You know I've had no sex with him for the last two years?'

I said nothing. Jeffrey'd told me one night at the factory that he was incapable of sex, a sure sign he was very ill. Guys who make art based on the fantasy of sexual looseness often have very sad sexual situations in their own homes. Romi was young enough and attractive enough, she'd gone to Japan to consider her options. When the bad news from Hanoi reached her, she'd already decided to end her personal relationship with Mr Gun Club. She soldiered on in the unforeseen circumstances but back in London she spent hours on the phone to Jesse stressing that it was over between her and the fat boy.

Days later phones began to hop with Nip accusation, malevolence and gossip.

Romi was complaining about Nigel doing junk on the road.

Kaz was saying she wasn't getting laid by Nigel.

Jeffrey was saying Romi was a beautiful young woman and deserved a fulfilling sex life.

Romi was saying life with Jeffrey was hell.

The Jap flatmates were telling Jeffrey that I was a bad band manager.

Jeffrey was bitching about me to Jesse.

And on and on. Suddenly we were starring in our own soap opera.

A visit to Jeffrey Lee's house was on the cards. He was recovering from his injuries, had been back in London a while licking his wounds, and courtesy demanded that we drop around.

When we did summon up the courage to visit, we were surprised by what we saw. His face was a bit battered—he had the remains of a few war wounds—but dysentery had done great things for his weight problem. He looked just like the angry young punk kid who'd launched The Gun Club onto the world, and a lot less like the self-pitying, boring slob we'd grown accustomed to. He was animated, alert, aware of what was happening in the real world, mean, ugly, lippy—even thin. He was wearing nice clothes; his track suits and raincoats were elsewhere. There was less talk about the blues, but multiple denunciations of the Vietnamese: 'Those fucking people! When I think of the things I said about those stupid ignorant people! They deserved every fucking thing they ever got...I'm never going back there ever again. All my life I've supported them and seen their point of view and this is what fucking happens to me!'

He'd expected them to collectively go: *Oh, there goes Jeffrey Lee Pierce from The Gun Club. He's really cool and seriously pro-Vietnamese. Don't touch him. He's not like all those other Yankees. He is in the tradition of all the great master blues musicians.*

When Nigel heard of Jeffrey's misfortunes, he was delighted for two weeks. He saw Jeffrey as a Falstaffian figure at the best of times, had Oriental follies going on in his own marital life, and he had stood in that Top of The Pops spotlight at least twice, something denied to Jeffrey Lee in his musically brilliant career. The two of them seemed like young practitioners right then, but they'd played snakes and ladders with the music industry the longest time, midnight gamblers on a midnight train. They'd been to sugartown, shook the sugar down. There was a cold zany/tragic equilibrium between them that was lost on Jesse and me.

Those were intensely creative days for Jeffrey, oddly enough. Most of the albums from The Gun Club's golden age were patchy affairs that captured the imagination of disenchanted weirdoes (like Jesse) all over the world. Now that nobody was interested, he addressed remarkable records to a shrunken universe as became a great bluesman.

I'm not prejudiced. I didn't like him.

Jeffrey didn't have a fax machine so an important, top secret document got faxed to his LA agent by Kaz from the MTV offices. Nigel discovered it in Kaz's flat one night he crashed there. I could've faxed it from the factory, but this ten page tract was not the class of thing a fallen idol wanted former fans or putative collaborators to see. Typed on Jeffrey's dinky portable typewriter, it disclosed the kind of man he was, why he was able to hold his own amid the shifting sands of popularity and intellectuality. First was a lean cool assessment of exactly where The Gun Club were going, pursuing a dwindling and not necessarily smart audience in Europe while, day by day, their American status went up in smoke.

After that, with a touch the Hemingwayesque prizefighter, the document suggested a solution: a co-ordinated North American re-launch centred on a 2CD compilation of tracks from the years in exile. On the back of this album The Gun Club, featuring both Romi and Kid Congo, could tour and publicise themselves. It was part business document, part fuel-injected autobiography. Given his health, Jeffrey Lee Pierce should have turned to writing.

Things fell apart between us when Nigel went to jail. The attacks on me came in hot and heavy because Jeffrey thought that he saw something of himself in me. One night, complaining about Romi, he phoned me: 'I know you understand what I'm going through, being an older man yourself.'

Eventually it unravelled completely, his Jap retinue of little sisters manipulating a crazy falling man. Jeffrey took to phoning Jesse in the middle of the night to say that Subliminal Kids' management problems (me) made it difficult for him to produce the band: 'Jesse, I know we could make a risky extreme record that'd be like…Blind Willie Davis…preaching music…but…I know you have a lot of respect for Kim and but he's totally untogether, he doesn't have a phone where people can contact him. He doesn't have a fax machine.'

The Gun Club had been the seed influence on Jesse as a young boy and the music he made was an affirmation of the seditionary running-wild-with-vampires-and-coons-through-the-swamp-city-jungle sensibility that Jeffrey invented out of his crazy mind. Jesse was correct to think then, and to still believe today, that the album they might've made together would have been fascinating music.

Perhaps I should have stepped out of the way, but there were other obstacles.

In the end Jeffrey left a memorable message on our answering machine saying he'd tear me apart limb from limb with his bare fists if I ever insulted him or his little sisters again. LX drove us round to his place. I sat in the Volvo, watching proceedings from the street while the two boys went to the front door to attempt a reconciliation. Jeffrey must have seen us coming because two seconds after LX rang the bell he came storming out, trembling with fury and abhorrence. On the verge of hysteria, he kept peering nervously over the hedge at the Volvo and at me. If he ever saw me again, he told Jesse as he eyed me in the near distance, he'd kill me. The Marlon Brando imitation was in full effect. He was mumbling, portly in a kaftan, and I knew he'd never get to produce Subliminal Kids now.

Jesse saw Romi in Notting Hill from time to time. The Gun Club abandoned an American comeback tour—in the middle of the tour—in support of the 2CD mentioned in the fax because Jeffrey was too ill to do the gigs. Kid Congo quit the band. When Nigel died and shit about him being a junkie appeared in the rock press, Jesse asked Romi if Jeffrey'd like to give us a quote for a press release. Jeffrey wouldn't come on the phone but passed on a message that he wasn't sure he was interested in saying anything nice about Nigel but would be happy to speak to any journalists who wanted

to ring him to talk about it. He didn't show up for the funeral either but sent his apologies later.

None of this would have surprised Nigel. Nigel always said he was an asshole.

We're south of Brixton in Dave Goodman's studio. I'm twitchy, the clock is running on my money: I've hired the studio for four days which is all the money I've got. Goodman was the Sex Pistols' soundman on their tours. He co-produced *The Great Rock'n'Roll Swindle* and is responsible for a lot of these dodgy semi-bootleg *Sex Pistols Live* albums you see on market stalls and in £2.99 CD shops.

Just in case you don't get the message he has his gold disc for Swindle up behind the mixing desk in his studio.

Just in case you don't get the message Glen Matlock strolls into the studio one day while we're there, all weird and intelligent.

I hate The Sex Pistols but that's not the point.

Nigel's on remand so we're using LX's brother again. It'll be a six track album, *Venceremos*; the idea is to do five new three minute songs and a cover version. It's Subliminal Kid's third album and Jesse likes to include a cover version on each album by way of a signature. This time it's *Be Thankful For What You Got* by the legendary, destructive, tragically romantic Arthur Lee and Love. It's a true signature.

Goodman is on a New Age trip, trying to get a record deal for three leggy acoustic blonde babes. He has loads of money, his home is all imitation antique furniture—can you spend a quarter of a million in Woolworths? He owns the house next door which is rented out to a tight-trousered metal band called Snake London. To differentiate them, I guess, from a dodgy going-nowhere nigger chanteuse called Snake.

I don't know about this South London trip. London south of Brixton is full of suburbanites who've settled for domestic comfort in lieu of inner city blues or civilisation.

I don't know about working with Goodman. I think he's siding with LX against Jesse which is both stupid and destructive. If Jesse's not happy with the finished tracks he'll dump them—after all, it's just five three minute songs. *Venceremos* is a record we actually need to put out, not some abstract experiment in finding out how fucked up LX can sound.

Cheap holidays at other people's misery, indeed!

So the two of us are sitting in My Way Mansions exchanging glances. We had a phenomenal row last night about nothing so we're not speaking. Loyal employees of Subliminal Kids Inc., we communicate on a subliminal level, with strong opinions of what the music should be like. No words are necessary. This session ain't going our way.

What would Sid Vicious do if he was here?

I'm staring at the reel to reel, the tape going round and round, LX smiling like a moron, my money going down the tube. I don't think Goodman shares our passion for motherfucker rock'n'roll.

The Sex Pistols never meant shit to me, you see.

If punk means anything, it means: Fuck this. Fuck that. Fuck you. You fucking brat.

Jazz emotions

I'm reading a book and it says that in 1925 in Cincinnati, Ohio the Salvation Army got a temporary injunction preventing the building of a motion picture theatre alongside the Catherine Booth Home for Girls, on the grounds that the music emanating from the theatre would implant *jazz emotions* in babies born in the home.

Yesterday I got to witness some Brixton jazz emotions. There was this mixed race couple in front of me on the 2A bus leaving Stockwell and heading towards Brixton, down by the side of the Brixton Academy.

He was an interesting looking twentyish black dude with a very sensitive face, big sensual lips and a cheap black suit. She was a beautiful white junkie girl in her mid-teens. She was filthy and smelled pretty bad but she was sexy and thin to perfection with hardly any tits at all like a perfect junkie whore/queen. She was the kind of girl I like for long fuck sessions up the back passage, for all intents and purposes a dog and not a human. From the way she was talking it seemed to me that she came from a pretty Up There background. I love licking the damp area between cunt and butthole. I love the skin down there. Special skin. That girl was extrasexual, most unusual in some way, and she dressed seriously.

Anyway her man turns to her and in that sweet macho voice that the homey favours, he says to her: 'Why are you crying?' and she replies: 'I'm not crying,' sounding like she's lying. 'I'm not crying. My eyes are sore.'

The dude is no fool and he knows right there right then that his Aryan junkie bitch sex slave is a two-timing whore. The difference between her and the Eiffel Tower is that they can work out how many people have been up the Eiffel Tower.

'No, your eyes are teary,' he murmurs slothfully. 'Those are tears.'

Neither spoke after that and I got off the bus in Brixton.

Last of the mohicans

It's the same walk, but my feet gets weary and weak.

When I get back to Berlin I pull out the old cardboard boxes full of the notebooks and tapes I've kept from Brixton.

The boxes are covered in stickers and full of ephemera. A three inch circular red and black sticker for Nicaragua says NO U.S. INTERVENTION under a graphic featuring Sandino. I bought it at a Third World fair in Brixton Town Hall. There's a Slayer sticker I got free with *Kerrang*. A flyer for a Subliminal Kids gig at Planet Rock in Paris on which I've written: 'And she said *Please don't blame the ugly ones for what the pretty ones do*.' Diary entries, notes on conversations, tapes of conversations, history salvaged from the pyre.

There's an old message book that LX maintained alongside his phone for what came in during the course of the day:

2.15   Noko. She wants to cancel her English lesson. Will ring in later.

3.40   Nigel to say he'll be late for the rehearsal. He sends his love.

5.05   Jeffrey rang. He'll be in London for the next two months. No tours.

5.15   Kim's mother called. Will he call her back?

5.20   Jesse, your brother called. He's going to score. Do you want anything? You can get a new 'Shadow' pickup at Brixton music shop.

5.50   Nigel can't make it to the rehearsal. 'Have I been fired or what?'

6.15   Noko. Do you want to come over for dinner tonight?

6.30   Rodrigo Gomez wants to come up and use the phone tomorrow. Is that cool?

6.40   Nigel will be at his folks' place all night if you want to call him.

7.16   Philippe for Kim. There's a party at Toshiba's place. Simone Semen is going to be there. Do you want to go? He thinks Kim should.

I note how busy the phone got in the early evening. That's when everybody got up and came to life. Those notebooks bring back my memories. I tend to live in the present and future, it's difficult to relate to the man I was then; so much went down in the flood that, as a squatter once said to me, it's a heavy trip on the brain.

The notebooks are in large ledger-style business diaries for 1983. I found a crate of them in a skip just down the road from Fitz's Willesden squat after a party early on in our London days. I imagined when I wrote them that they'd be important one day. We began the tapes when we were going through a five month William Burroughs phase of experiments with tape. Some of the tapes are diaries of our days. Others are self-consciously witty or arch or naked. We had it in mind to use the stuff for songs and for writing. Sometimes I'd switch on the tape recorder when Jesse wasn't looking and vice versa.

On the back of this awful nostalgia I organise a dinner party for the following Saturday. Screw, the friend who gave us the factory, still lives in Berlin where he works with Rodrigo Gomez; it was Screw who introduced me to Rodrigo in the first place. They have a big international punk t-shirt business going together now. They don't look like punks or *NME* readers any more—they look like relatively young t-shirt millionaires. Nowadays I don't slap the tape recorder on the dining room table. I'm more discreet.

Gomez gets there first, saying Screw will be late; his new kid has a fever and they're waiting for the doctor to come. So me and Gomez drink a lot of wine, I turn the stew down low to simmer and we wait. Screw reaches us by taxi around 10.30, we eat, and I pull out my notebooks and pass them around. Reading that stuff throws them into shock and forces them to be sentimental too. That was back in the days.

Jah Screw: I'd love to see your photographs from Brixton, Kim, I'd love to be reminded of what you looked like then.

Kim: There are no photographs of us from that time.

Jah Screw: Why the fuck not?

Kim: Well… we didn't have a camera. Nobody ever bought one for us and…anyway…I looked like shit.

Jah Screw: Man, you and Jesse, you were both so out of it in those days...

Kim: We were, but we knew that we were. It was a self-conscious thing. You know Jesse always says it was important for us to spend those years in London, to do all that talking. He says Plato never wrote anything, that Plato just talked and his students took notes. Jesse reckons he lived for the future then and that now the future is upon him.

Jah Screw: How's he going now?

Kim: He keeps good, has a nice apartment in the middle of Madrid. When I'm in Algeciras I sometimes take a D train to Madrid and stay with him for a week. Sometimes he comes down to Algeciras and we head off to Morocco to do a lot of ganja.

Jah Screw: So he's never changed.

Kim: Oh, he changed. He has a little money now. Look at us. We all have a little money, a blessing and a curse. He has more time to think things over before he does them. I guess that's called old age. Back in Brixton every day was in flux; you never know who was going to knock on the door next, the Pigs, the electricity people— you never knew how the day would end. I don't think we were paranoid but we were under a certain sort of pressure all the time. When things started going right we didn't have the infrastructure to handle it. It's OK changing your phone number all the time if you're just in the business of burning down lines and shit. But when you've got a band that's going somewhere, Regular Guy business assholes start getting worried if they find you're disconnected.

Rodrigo: And some of those guys you surrounded yourselves with, that dude LX, he was a shifty character. When I'd call up to use the phone he'd be so convoluted. It was so difficult to get a straight answer out of him. 'Where's Kim?' and he'd say 'Oh, he's somewhere. I haven't seen him for days myself.' And then you'd walk through the door and it'd turn out that you'd been with LX all morning. I kind of liked him all the same.

Kim: I kind of liked him myself. Jesse and he had a lot of problems to do with the band, which was their main interaction. Jesse hassled and hassled and hassled the kid. In one way this was fair enough because he never got his guitar shit together. We didn't know it at the time but this chick who was going out with his brother, the surf bum kid who used to stand in for Nigel? I met up with her years later when I was living in Clerkenwell and she was doing computer stuff for a photographic agency. She says that LX was robbing us towards the end of the time we were squatting in Ralston House. I mean, I don't really hold it against him, can't anyway, but there were a few weird robberies of peripheral squats.

Jah Screw: How many flats did you fuckers have squatted?

Kim: At the height of it all Jesse had about twenty apartments under his control—he was kind of a squat real estate agent, quite out of sympathy with the thinking of your hardcore anarcho-squatters. We had the place we shared with one another. I had another place of my own, and Jesse had one too. We had two very big flats we used solely for storage. We'd break into a place and strip it of anything like cookers or fridges or decent bits of furniture such as beds and things. Jesse's main clients were Brazilians who were straight enough middle class types. One guy who had a wife and child was an Up There classical musician back home—he'd done an album for EMI Brazil. He was in London working in an office, earning about £350 a week, his wife doing the same. They just wanted to save every penny so they could go home to Brazil after working for two years and buy a farm with their savings. They wanted to squat, not pay rent. But they were illegals in England and if they'd even been questioned by the Pigs they'd just have been frog-marched out to the airport and sent home. Jesse had this deal going with a lot of Brazilians. They needed somebody to do their breaking and entering for them. They'd give him £200 for a squat with a new lock on it, and then they'd shell out more money for fridges and cookers and what have you. That was how Jesse made a living. I had my own businesses going with LX. Anyway, this was the thing, LX started robbing the Brazilians and the Italian junkies and other sorts that Jesse was providing with homes. Eventually he started robbing niggers' flats too, and that was a whole other problem. LX's brother—the drummer—was so different, so straight, so clean...he became a Christian later.

Rodrigo: A Christian! What the fuck did LX make of that? He wasn't exactly the spiritual type.

Kim: LX was dead by then. I think it was LX's death that turned the brother Christian.

Rodrigo: I didn't know LX died...oh...shit...I used to see so much of him when we were there...

Kim: Yeah...poor old LX got killed about three months after I left Brixton. The last thing I did with him, between the time I moved to Kensal Rise and when he died, was a cocaine importation scam. LX had this really filthy squat on another estate—it had nothing to do with Jesse—that I used for storage and as a mail drop. I'd met this Bolivian woman through our dealer Boycott. She came from the side of a mountain in Bolivia where her brothers had a cocaine machine or what the fuck. So every week these little envelopes would arrive from the side of the mountain full of noxious damp pure coke. LX would collect the packets and we'd knock it out fast, adding about 75% additives. At the same time, LX had a variety of different deals going down with other people which were his own business. But he was doing way, way too many different powders and, being a country bumpkin, lacked a certain wariness when it came to doing business with the nigger. Anyway, he got real pissed off with Jesse in the last three months of his life and quit Subliminal Kids. Which was a pity as far as I was concerned but Jesse says getting rid of a B-division guitarist set the Kids free. And it is true that after LX departed things really started moving…LX would have been leaving the band anyway, as it transpired. I saw him on a Tuesday and when I phoned him over the next three days there was never any reply, just the answering machine. This was not like him at all and the machine was clogging up with messages so I took a trip down to see him and he'd disappeared. A few days later his body was found at the end of a deserted warehouse pier down in Docklands, one of the undeveloped parts. The Pigs said it was drug-related so they did a perfunctory investigation, the results of which they passed on to his folks. His mother told me the bones of it. He'd been in way out of his league, involved with this white drug gang working out of South London, who he'd met through this dealer Jay that lived under us. He also got to know some very bigtime nigger suppliers and was involved with them in a scam to rip off his white brothers. End of poor old LX.

Jah Screw: Shit, man, you and Jesse seem to have gotten into some pretty scary scenes after I quit town. A *lot* of men died.

Kim: They died. And it made us think. Unnecessary deaths of young men. Nigel dying and LX dying...we'd lived with them. I was more or less indifferent about Jeffrey Lee dying because if you'd seen the miserable life he had...you'd have wanted to die too.

Jah Screw: Me and Lisa, wow, we loved The Gun Club. *Fire of Love* and *Wildweed* were such wonderful albums, so different from what everybody else was at. When you sent me the postcard saying you were hanging with Jeffrey Lee I was just so impressed.

Rodrigo Gomez: When I quit LA The Gun Club were gods. They were the coolest band to catch at The Roxy on a Saturday.

Kim: Yeah...well...he was an impressive lunatic. I didn't like him but he did some fantastic records and songs. Do you know *St John Divine* or *Yellow Eyes*?

Jah Screw: Nah, was that the later period?

Kim: Yeah, the Romi years. I think he called a retrospective CD of those days *In Exile*, which is what the poor fucker was. *Yellow Eyes* was about himself, you know? The jaundice caused by his liver...because of the junk. *Yellow Eyes, don't be afraid.* I guess he was afraid...You know Lisa phoned me last week? She seems to be doing pretty OK.

Jah Screw: She does good. She's gone totally California. She says she's organising a benefit concert for some local good cause. I think they want to open a cybercafe in our daughter's school. So she *has* changed...what'd you think of Lady Di snuffing it?

Kim: Well...she was screwing an Arab...what can you expect...d'you hear what Keith said when they asked the Stones to contribute to some tribute album? 'I never met the chick.'...oh, you know, I reckon she was snuffed out completely.

Rodrigo: Yeah, motherfucker. I guess when the Queen got the word up in Scotland that she was dead they woke up the fucking piper and had him playing jigs and reels on top of the dining room table.

Kim: Man, you fucking wetback asshole! Take a bow wow wow!

I walk the line

We flew to Dublin to show off our new drummer. It was a big deal in a provincial dump like Dublin that we'd a star from The Cult in the Kids. Those were Preston's first gigs with us, and it seemed appropriate to start a new chapter back in the old town.

Right then The Cult were living in America, authentic rock superstars fighting it out with the biggest stadium bands, produced by the mighty hip hop producer Rick Rubin (The Beastie Boys! LL Cool J!), enjoying the fantasy that being in a hot group offers. *She Sells*

Sanctuary, their awful but memorable hit single, remained their most successful track.

The band travelled to Ireland by van and ferry, I flew cheapo with Ryanair. Mid-afternoon I reached the house we were staying in, a new townhouse with a cool entry-phone system owned by the father of a groupie, this wretched California creature I called Squeaky in honour of Squeaky Fromme, Charles Manson's demented murderous lady companion. There was no sign of the Kids, so I settled down to eating Squeaky's vegetarian frozen food and watching MTV on her TV.

The first gig was pencilled in for that evening and the van eventually showed up at 7PM with four exhausted and irritated musicians. The problem was Nigel, who'd nodded off in the back of the van as they got on the ferry in Wales. Falco, who was driving, tried in vain to rouse him when the van was parked in the hold but in the end they left him there sleeping. Hours later, when they got back into the van to disembark in Dublin, Preston was still on the nod and no amount of kicking, tickling, or shouting woke him.

This would have been fine if Customs hadn't decided to give our van a thorough once-over. When they opened the back doors of the van they found, amid the amps, guitars and drums, a comatose Nigel. They removed a big guitar amp to get a better look at him and he fell out of the van and onto the tarmac.

This made a very bad impression, especially since Nigel kept sleeping. Subliminal Kids were frog-marched off to a customs shed where they were questioned for an hour while Customs attempted to wake Nigel up. Eventually he surfaced, with helpful questions like 'Where the fuck am I?' and, to a senior Customs asshole: 'Who the fuck are you? You Irish cunt.' This got him taken to one side where he was stripsearched and arse-probed by a youngish officer who took pleasure in his task, fully aware of who The Cult were.

The gig went funky but chic, LX and Falco playing with rather than against one another, Preston defining the night through his rhythms. Squeaky organised a Welcome Home party back at her townhouse, and I went to bed around 7AM. Nigel and me had to share a bedroom, indeed a double bed.

He headed off relatively early. When I climbed into the bed hours later he was all alone, but not sleeping. He was in a cranky half-sleep interrupted by small fits of upful giggling. Eventually it turned weirder and it was impossible to tell if he was feeling bad or good. He needed to talk.

'Kim, where can you score junk in Dublin?'

'Anywhere, but most conveniently on the main street, O'Connell Street.'

'When am I going to meet your old girlfriends?'

'Never. I left Ireland to forget them!'

'Did you know my brother plays rugby with London Irish?'

'Yeah, Nigel, of course I do.'

'Kim, did you enjoy the gig tonight?'

'Yeah I did. I was really proud of you Preston, you played really good.'

'Where are we playing tomorrow night?'

Preston kept getting out of bed, walking all over the house, returning to bed, instigating further conversations with me about music; how beautiful the Irish girls were, drugs he liked more than others, what sort of character Jesse was; and so many other irritations that I eventually got out of bed resentfully and watched CNN in the living room until everyone else got up.

Nigel remained edgy and tough for the rest of the Irish week. He drummed like a young dreamer, fulfilling all the hopes and expectations that Jesse and I shared for rock music and Subliminal Kids.

Onstage it was great to have him in our ranks, and he was happy doing club gigs where he could see the skate kids moshing, the diabolic spirit summoned, the young boys flying through the air like salmon going upstream. He said when The Cult got really popular he had to avert his gaze from the front rows where the ugliest cretins gathered in adulation. Offstage he was always hunting for heavy-duty shit, strangely asexual to the extent that I wondered if he was gay.

Today I know more about the sensibilities of the junkie, then an Oriental land to me. I liked the country, but I couldn't speak the language or share the religion. I don't mind people knowing what I used to be like. I reveal that part of me and people think I'm telling them about myself.

After the tour I travelled south to see my family for a week and the Kids returned to England by ferry.

When I flew back to London the Ralston House squat looked like a combat zone. Nigel and Jesse had been partying since returning to London and, while I'd been in the bourgeois embrace of family, they'd gone back on the cutting edge, the frontline, the firing line. My bedroom was totally fucked up, home for a week to The King of Narcotics who'd managed to make it through the night without selling off my books and records.

When Nigel finally cleared off to his parents' place Jesse told me what had happened in my absence. The afternoon they got back from Ireland Jesse woke up and went into my bedroom to find Nigel gone. He was in the middle of making breakfast when a flushed and agitated rock legend started thumping the front door, howling 'Jesse! Jesse! Let me in you fucker!'

Jesse opened the door to find a triumphant Preston standing there, two large plastic bags full of bottles of whiskey, gin and vodka in his hands. He'd gone around the corner to Patel's shop and used an imitation revolver to rob Patel.

'Empty the till you Paki fucker,' he reported himself as saying. He jubilantly pulled a couple of hundred quid from his pocket, walked over to the phone and called LX, who was still asleep. 'Wake up you little bitch,' he laughed. 'We've got money and I want you to drive me to a reputable dealer I know down the Barrier Block. And if you want any of these drugs you can give your drummer and Master a blowjob each.'

'So he and LX went off to some dealer Nigel knew and I got ready for the hurricane,' Jesse cackled to me. 'When they got back they had the whole cocktail. Scag, crack, cocaine.'

'Did LX give you the blowjobs?'

'No, of course not!' said Jesse, cracking up. 'Not that I'd leave that wretch near my knob in any case. Mind you, he and Nigel did disappear for a while…Anyway, that's entirely irrelevant. What was interesting, however, was the shit I found out about Nigel in the next few days. He's been involved with this North London criminal gang that specialise in armed robbery since he was a teenager. I get the impression they're big-time, and Nigel is their getaway driver. He swore me to secrecy because these boys are the real thing, some way connected to Mad Tim Taylor.'

'The old fucker who used to be pulling out guys' nails

and putting their hands into deep fat fryers?'

'The very one.'

'Tim Taylor! Son of a gun!'

Yellow eyes

Six months ago I was reading a book, *Americana 1926* edited by the great HL Mencken, when Jesse phoned. We don't see each other too much anymore but we talk on the phone nearly every day. Just before the phone rang I was reading an item discovered by Mencken in *Weekly Unity*, the magazine in the Twenties of the Higher Life cult in Kansas City:

"Insects are the result of error ideas of life and wrong uses of the life forces by man. When Divine Order is established in man's thoughts and in his life, order will manifest also in the outer, and insects that prey upon vegetables, animals and man will disappear. As man grows in understanding and in truth he will be troubled less and less by flies, mosquitoes and bugs."

Jesse: Did you hear the news about Jeffrey Lee?

Kim: Nah, I don't think so.

Jesse: Well, I met with this PR guy at a club last night and he was telling me this incredible story about Jeffrey Lee. Wait till I tell you.

Kim: All stories about Jeffrey Lee are totally incredi-

ble. *I ran into him about three months ago in Notting Hill. He was checking out some amps in the Record and Tape Exchange. So I waited outside until he came out and then I walked on by and said, 'Hi, Loser!' and he stamps his feet and screams at me, 'You fucking asshole!!'*

Jesse: Did he attack you with his machete?

Kim: What?

Jesse: Shut the fuck up and I'll tell you what. This guy I was talking with was Jeffrey's booking agent and was, kind of, his legal guardian in the UK. In order for Jeffrey to get a visa to live there, this agent had to sign papers saying that Jeffrey was in regular work, the agency were employing him, or some shit like that. It was all very legal; the dude had to give the authorities his home address and phone number. So last week in the middle of the night he gets a phonecall from Heathrow. Jeffrey Lee was being held there in some sort of holding cell, about to be deported to America for assaulting some guy in Notting Hill with a machete.

Kim: A machete? Oh fuck!

Jesse: Some Oriental thing he had. It seems he'd been drinking heavily all day.

Kim: Jeffrey Lee can't drink with his liver all fucked up.

Jesse: Exactly. And there's the rub. Apparently he's

been drinking all the time for the last five months. He kind of disbanded The Gun Club and has been showing up totally out of it, singing with Shane McGowan at Nick Cave gigs. Romi finally got around to leaving him and has gone off with some guitarist. Jeffrey was drinking alone in that fucking dump on the corner of Notting Hill Gate and Pembridge Road. Apparently he spent the whole day there drinking and got into a big boozey argument with some moron he met. It was a heavy heavy scene and the bar staff fired him out. He stormed off home in high dudgeon where he got this Oriental machete, headed back to the pub, and attacked the guy with the machete...

Kim: Mother of Jesus...did he cut the guy?

Jesse: Many times, but none too seriously. He emptied the place, it goes without saying, and ended up doing thousands of pounds worth of damage. They sent for the Pigs and vanloads of them arrived and arrested Jeffrey. He was hauled off to the station and charged with, you know...whatever...assault, attempted murder, possession of a weapon, you name it. They frog-marched him off to a holding unit out at Heathrow, which is where the dude I met came across him. He says Jeffrey was subdued and depressed when he got to him. He brought him some clothes and stuff, but there was fucking nothing he could do to keep him in the country. The vibe was that he was either going to be sent off to America or charged with all this shit.

Kim: So Jeffrey is actually back in America right now?

Jesse: Back in America. Where he should have been all along. Where his music fucking comes from.

Kim: Yeah, it's true. Jeffrey should never have lived in England. And all his stuff...his guitars...his gear, his things?

Jesse: Oh well, the Japs are still in the flat, except for Romi who has gone working for Vidal Sassoon, so his stuff is still safe. He's living with his mother, apparently.

Did I hear what happened to Jeffrey Lee? Yeah, I did.

Jeffrey Lee Pierce ended up back in California where I heard reports through mutual pals in the music business that he put together a new line-up of The Gun Club, a *real* Gun Club, meaning it contained Kid Congo Powers. He did a lot of gigs in California and they say the music was fresh and new, the magic of the old days returned. He kept on leading the reckless hard-living life that characterised his final days in England and the long-ago wild crazy days of his youth.

He went to visit his father in hospital when the old man had a stroke. While visiting, he got a stroke himself and was rushed into hospital in LA, where he lived on for a while, visited by his old friends including Kid Congo who reported that he was serene and aware that he was dying. And then he died.

A month after I heard the news I bought the German language edition of *Rolling Stone* in Berlin because it had a long review of the new Subliminal Kids album. Three pages of the same issue were given over to a respectful obituary of Jeffrey. It said he'd blended psychotic Delta blues, demented rockabilly and murky alternative visions of reality, cited his influence over whole generations of less talented rock groups like Nirvana and U2, and suggested that Gun Club titles like *Sex Beat* and *She's Like Heroin to Me* gave you the gist of the Gun Club's message.

How ironic that he should go down as Jesse is going up. I guess that's why they call it the blues.

Rap

Hard to be a pretty boy,
When you're a city boy.
Cock protrudin'.
Hips attituding.
Cock getting copped by the queers in bus station.
Straight white youth versus the queer nation.
Babylon is burning and there's no water.

Babylon burning. There's no water.
Work the bus station.
Victim of the queer nation.
Always said you liked pussy.
With guys you were more fussy.
You like them straight and tall,
Like them up against the wall.
Cup a hand round their balls.
Nine inches of fire.
Then you're on desire.
Babylon's burning and there's no water.
Babylon's burning and there's no water.
Hard to be a pretty boy,
If you're a city boy.
Your joint getting copped
By the queers on the prowl.
Babylon burning. There's no water.

Something in a something

The band took off quick. Most weekends there were good paying gigs. Obscurity gave way to cult status. You don't know what you've got till it's gone.

We were due to do a long-weekend tour of Cornwall so Jesse pencilled in rehearsals for Tuesday and Wednesday. He'd written some new songs he wanted to try out on the Cornwallers. Nigel didn't show up Tuesday, which was no surprise since he was proving to be an inspired but unreliable Subliminal Kid. Wednesday afternoon LX woke up late to find a chipper upbeat message from Nigel on his answering machine: 'I'm at Paddington police station but don't worry. I'll call you later this evening.'

Jesse looked up Nigel's folks' number in the phone book and had the first of several conversations with his parents, neither of whom we'd met. It was the first they'd heard of Nigel's arrest—he was only allowed one phonecall and he made that, honourably enough, to his band. He'd been a musician long enough to understand band loyalty though his relationship with his folks was a very warm and real one, unlike his marriage which was downright weird. Kaz was a presenter with MTV Japan and lived in a spacious Hampstead apartment while he was the archetypal penniless rock musician constantly borrowing tenners from her, Jesse, even LX.

Working for the music fantasy factory, Kaz's interiority was dominated by rock iconography. Nigel was a past his sell-by date exhibit in her museum, curated while he was a glistening trophy. Kaz was very pally with Kurt Cobain and Nirvana—then a big club band—and talked about moving to Seattle; Cobain was another interesting dude who didn't last forever either.

Nigel had been arrested several times before for drink, drug and affray style offences. In The Cult he'd decked a shop assistant who refused to accept his credit card. Used to these incidents, his family said he'd be out on police bail by nightfall but it proved more serious than that; he was in a lot more trouble than usual. He'd repeated his Patel routine up in Kilburn, emptied the till with his imitation revolver, and tried to make his getaway by tube. Some right-wing old English bitch saw him leaving the off license in disarray, stuffing money into one pocket and the gun into another, so she followed him to the tube station. The bitter old bitch went to a phone booth and called the cops.

They got in touch with the tube and stopped all trains going in or out of the station. Nigel, sitting on the platform for ten minutes waiting for a train, was thinking it was taking a long time for one to come when he saw the Pigs approaching him. He was arrested and hauled off to the station where they kicked him all over the place, adding assault on a police officer to the robbery charges.

He disappeared inside the English prison system for eighteen months in all. A remorseless process began that day which ended with his death. We headed off to Cornwall where LX's brother—a six foot, blonde and blue eyed, surf kid-cum-drumming prodigy—learned off the set in three hours.

I got a good hard look at the justice system via Nigel. Before his case came to court I went to see him in a north

London police station where they were holding him in state of the art Thatcherite conditions. In one large modern block they had a courthouse, a cop shop and a holding unit with cells for a hundred prisoners on remand. The station had been built in the previous two years—you could still smell the fresh paint, the newly sawed wood, the mortar: freshness you don't normally associate with jail.

Greater love hath no man—I walked through seven electronically controlled security doors, under endless surveillance cameras, and past more Pigs than I'd ever met in my entire life to get near him. The purported reason for the visit was that I was Preston's manager and had to discuss urgent legitimate business with him.

Dressed in clothes I'd probably been wearing for five years, my hair uncut since the early Eighties, my squatter paranoia was in the house.

The year Nigel Preston went down I was on the outer fringes of society. Except for that one brief trip to see my folks in rural Ireland, I'd not been in many sitting rooms, dining rooms or even homes for three years. I'd not been to an art gallery, a shopping centre, a laundromat, a shoe shop, a dentist, a doctor, a hardware store, a men's clothes shop or a hi-fi store for the same amount of time. I remembered how to speak English, I had all the new hip hop records that came out, and that was about the size of it. I don't think the

Pigs really thought I had a whole lot of business to discuss with Nigel.

We had our sad little meeting on a harsh wooden bench in a spare cell, a young blonde cop sitting opposite us on another bench, his sharp eyes moving from one of us to the other, like a chatshow camera, while we spoke. We both set out to annoy him. Preston was chipper enough—there was no need to feel sorry for him. Being locked up was not the same human tragedy for him that it was for me, he'd been locked up by the State many times before. He was really on the fringe, I just chose to squat there.

'So who's been to see you Nigel?'

'My mum, my dad, my brothers. That's about the size of it. He smirked proudly, sardonically.

'Has Kaz been in?' I sometimes wondered if that was her real name. Jeffrey's Japs operated under false names.

'Nah, Kim, I don't think Kaz will be in to see me. She thinks I've brought shame down around her,' he laughed.

He got three years and served a year in Pentonville Prison, a Victorian shithole which did him in. Visits to Pentonville involved smuggling him dope, listening to scurrilous tales of loneliness and degradation about various other prisoners he'd spot in the visitors' room while we were talking to him: 'That nigger over there comes from Zambia. Poor cunt hasn't a word of English, or at least if he has he doesn't let on. He's been here on remand for nine months, they've really locked *him* up and thrown away the key. Nobody visits him from one end of the month to the other except for that woman with him just now who is from some Christian charity that organises visits to guys like him.'

When he got out of Pentonville he relaxed into drink and drugs, was dark and bleak, allowing no compromise with friendship or civility. Falco, who quit the Kids when Nigel got locked up, would sometimes run into him in the George Robey, the dive where he'd first met him.

'He was really *so* out of it,' Falco reported on the phone one day, his German accent to the fore, 'and I don't think he knew where he was. I asked him how things were going with you guys and he said he was still playing with you. Is he?'

'Yeah, he is,' Jesse would always defend him. 'He is pretty untogether OK. I went to some gigs with him straight after he got out and he was totally fucked, not in control of himself at all...there were fights and arguments and most of the time he just wanted to rap about drugs, get drugs...but he still does our gigs. Just we can't get him to rehearse anymore. He is always promising the sun, moon and fucking stars but...it's all a bit abstract really.'

The truth was that he was finished, only I didn't spot it. He generally did make it to gigs, but the fact that he never showed up for rehearsals meant that the music was suffering. He'd always had a bad boy reputation which appealed to us, but that was now turning into a bad band reputation and it was only a matter of time before we got rid of him.

Twenty years a-growin'

Liam phones, he asks me if I want to go to a free party with him.

'You've never been to one of them before, have you?' says the plucky little cocksucker. I admit I've never seen one, hard going for me because I like to be the king of the hill. It's Liam's twentieth birthday and who am I to disagree with one so young, gifted and white? I'll go.

'I'll meet you in an hour,' I say, hanging up, dialling a minicab.

This particular number one scratch DJ lives in Camberwell, comes from Manchester, grandchild of Irish emigrants. His people came from Mayo. He goes to the School of Oriental and African Studies where he does Islamic Studies. Next year he goes to Egypt for a year. Being of urban Irish extraction he relates to the niggers—grew up with them in Manchester. I have a modicum of respect for this wild untrammelled city of Manchester, full of the victims of Thatcher's economic genocide. Liam intimidates me a little. It's the only reason I keep my distance.

(The Kids have a gig tomorrow night but I can party Friday night. Come Saturday I must manage in Stoke Newington.)

I arrive to find Liam, wearing a black Paul Smith t-shirt, wrapped up in his turntables, a lonely lover experimenting with the vinyl grooves. It's urban music straight from New York niggers and a Manchester Irishman.

Has the stylus replaced the guitar plectrum? I don't think so.

I bring him a birthday present—a copy of *Twenty Years A-Growing*, a translation from the Irish of *Fiche Blian Ag Fás*, a novel about growing up on the Irish-speaking west coast of Ireland. I explain that the title comes from a saying they have in the West: you spend twenty years a-growing, twenty years a-living, twenty years a-dying.

'So you're about to start your twenty years a-living,' I tell him; a *real* birthday present.

'Hmm,' he says, rejecting it, 'I prefer to think that I'm about to start my twenty years a-growing.'

Then he spins piles of 7-inch Jamaican pressings of the Cool Ruler, Lee Perry, Prince Buster. He rolls serial joints with the last of his dope. He comes from a generous generation. I don't.

Black rose,
In Jah's garden grows.

All reggaed-up, we hit the tube system and head towards the Central Line which'll bring us to North Acton. I've been there before. I went there to see a record distribution company—John B—about putting out an album by the Kids that the Sex Pistols producer produced. The guy in charge of international distribution at John B told me how to give myself a beer enema. Said it makes the beer go further.

We're on the last midnight train going west. It's packed with a motley crew—couples, commuters, drunks, ageing rockers, young marrieds. When we go beyond Notting Hill the crowd thins out and it's hardcore ravers versus those living beyond the central zones. They look at us dejectedly and we look back at them with contempt.

North Acton is the lonely industrial zone. Nobody lives there, people just go there to work every day, happy slaves. Liam's been to the venue before. 'It's just beyond the graveyard, like Heaven,' the Catholic boy says. 'We'll meet somebody who'll sell us some drugs. Don't worry.' The kids who get off the tube the same stop as us make their way towards the music in small huddled groups. The graveyard is to our left, as new as the industrial estate and just as busy.

I see an allnight garage up ahead so I go there to pick

up a Coke. Liam says he'll get some water inside so he stands on the footpath while I join the queue waiting to be served. Just five kids queue in front of me but it's taking forever. The cretin behind the bullet-proof glass isn't used to dealing with children of the revolution— after all he works a late night garage in the middle of a fucking industrial estate. I see Liam, a nervous control freak, trying to score drugs, talking to four or five people who don't seem connected.

Outlaws man the entrance to the party, and charge us two quid before letting us into an abandoned factory unit, about the size of two football pitches. In the distance I see a sound system and flashing white lights and strobes. No security, no paranoia, no hustle. About eight hundred people gather around the light and the sound. It's really simple, there is nothing slick about the lighting, but there's a neon urban elegance here. Elsewhere the vast darkness is partially relieved by the outside street lights.

Liam keeps on searching for drugs. I leave him alone for a while.

Stairs lead to three stories of disused offices, where the factory's business got done before the recession. There's no electricity here either but I'm so high up that I'm close to the street lights and can see everything clearly. Each floor has fifteen rooms separated by paper-thin plywood walls covered in wood-effect. In two rooms couples are screwing. In most, people are rolling joints or having elaborate conversations. By the time I get downstairs again Liam has bought us two Es each and we're off!

Liam disappears for an hour and I bump into Rodrigo Gomez who's even more into the music and out of it than me. He has a lovely redhaired girl called Molly with him. He wants to talk about running some parties like this one at the factory but I'm too out of it to talk about anything serious so I tell him to forget it until later. Last time I see Gomez he is heading towards the offices with little Molly.

Eight hours later the sound system's still playing the same tune (but me legs gets weary and weak). Liam is in perfect form, keeping quiet when that's appropriate and yapping like a fool when that, alternatively, is relevant.

Morning comes, the crowd is thinning out, it's time to go home. We pass the graveyard on the way back to the tube, freezing from both the cold and the energy we've used up. We spot a converted factory the size of an aircraft hangar painted fresh white, with the title JESUS HOUSE in huge plastic lettering over its entrance. It's a church now. A smaller sign says: 'People of all nations welcome.'

'*All nations*,' I say to Liam, 'means niggers.'

I take the Central Line with Liam, avoiding the eyes of the Sunday morning crowd until we catch a cab to

Camberwell where he has a rough comedown. He sleeps on his bed, I sleep on his couch. His flat is nice, more SOAS student than Manchester nigger. But he has a heart of darkness. Will he be so happy when he's a man? I don't think so.

Breakfast is a late afternoon conversation about dragging Liam to the gig. He says he knows nothing about white music, which means he doesn't want to go. I look out his sitting room window at the purple chemical sky while he gets back into bed with his turntables and fucks them senseless. I hit the streets at dusk.

I arrive after the band, travelling across town by train. I know they're there because the van is parked outside. I get in through an unguarded door, walk upstairs, and stroll into an empty hall. The guys have already set up their gear and are moving towards the task of soundchecking. A few characters are lurking in the background. A sort of demented hunchback—one of the barmen—who once chatted up a friend of mine claiming he played a monster in a Walt Disney movie, is polishing glasses.

They love us at this venue—Peggy Dell's—because we draw huge crowds, so therefore our strange nigger-loving ways are indulged by the normally racist Irish owner. The calm that precedes a gig where everybody is going to make lots of money is in the air. Love is in the air, a love called money.

Peggy Dell's, an old Irish ballroom, holds about six hundred people. Peggy Dell was an Irish Big Band singer in the Forties. When we go to the dressing room for a joint the owner—a pinstriped criminal fucker from Kerry—strolls in, sniffs the air, says 'Ah, lads!' He looks at me like I'm supposed to be the responsible one. I wonder what he makes of our Mr Preston, white skinned and sweaty.

I tell him I'm having an Ecstasy comedown and he says, 'Ah, that's grand.'

Time for the soundcheck. Jesse walks over to me and in rapid staccato says: 'I'm just going to do four numbers. Fast ones. Have you been talking to Preston? Did you see the state of him? He looks like shit. Did you have a good time last night? Did you get laid? I went to a shit party with LX.' With this he turns to LX and Preston, telling them it's time for the soundcheck.

The band's music went dull four years ago, but now life is returning. Jesse was right not to fall for the fallacy of reviving rock with the rhythms of hip hop. Instead he looked for a new route—travelled the barren hostile city and shot the future into his veins. Subliminal Kids used to have some songs that were seven or eight minutes long. Now everything is acutely brief, made of iron and steel. Now he has some sort of future and I have some kind of future.

Jesse always knew what he was doing. It just took

him a while. Me...I've seen the DJs.

An overweight, fortyish thug, an associate of the owner, well dressed in pricey casuals, sits at the bar sipping a pint. His companion, no pale companion, is thinner, younger and less well dressed in denim. They're in Peggy Dell's during the Kids' soundcheck—Irish assholes—but I know we'll be well paid tonight so I don't give a fuck if they want to sit around watching the boys make mistakes.

The fat older one comes over to me to ask if I manage the band. I say I do and he starts giving me shit like, 'Are they going to play *Rawhide*?' I tell him No. Is Jesse queer? No. Am I queer? No. Is that fella the drummer from The Cult? Yeah. Is it true he's a junkie? No. Is he queer? Eventually I tell him they haven't paid in, should just relax, enjoy the music or leave; or at least shut the fuck up and leave me alone. Fatso goes off disgruntled but *does* shut up. The band keeps on playing and sound-checking.

Jesse has taken on board the fact that LX is no virtuoso, while Preston is. Preston and Jesse work together like one animal so the rhythm section is built up and the guitar is just noise and feedback. There are no solos and the lyrics are rude and rough.

Put Jesse on stage and he behaves just like a human being. After the promised four songs—which last about two minutes each—he starts jamming old party things,

Ramones, Richard Hell, Blondie. With this soundtrack I make for the men's room to piss, an awful mistake.

I'm getting ready to leave the toilet when Fatso follows me in and starts giving me shit again. Says I'm a spoilsport, an asshole, and what's wrong with me. It's a reasonably good humoured slanging match. I say I'm anything but a spoilsport, that I enjoy 'sport' way too much for my own good. It's not a dangerous situation except that he's blocking the exit; I can't get around the big boy.

After five minutes we're leaving together when the younger thinner cocksucker joins us, deranged as he comes through the door, glaring at me full of malice. 'Why are you giving my friend grief, you fucking cunt?' he says as he headbutts me, causing blood to spurt out of my eyebrow. I'm stunned. Wounded, I almost faint. I look down to the ground for a second, notice the wet tiles, the smell of piss, steady myself. This is just like dying. By the time my eyes level with my attacker again, he's drawn a knife with an eight inch blade from the sleeve of his denim jacket and is about to stab me. I stare at the sharp, bright steel with fascination.

It's not the first time I've been in trouble with a weapon so I start talking to him, distracting his mutt-like attention from what he wants to do next. The real problem is that the venue is empty, the Kids are onstage playing through a full PA, nobody is ever going to walk into the toilet by accident. There's no point in shouting out—nobody'll hear me. I can hear Jesse singing one of his songs outside so he won't be coming to rescue me.

The psycho says he's going to stab me because I'm such a cunt. He talks and talks about cutting me, dwelling on the subject, studying the blade with frenzied narcoticised eyes. This rap continues for maybe three minutes—things going very badly for me—until his fat buddy starts intervening and tells him to cop on. Then they argue between themselves for a minute or two like criminals will while I'm standing there watching them, blood spurting from my wound. Eventually, due to the fat guy, the knife is put away and I'm told to get to fuck out of there and to say nothing to anybody about the incident. Or they'll come after me and settle me.

I walk back into the hall covered in blood, not badly hurt, aware that I almost got killed.

Deep Ellum

The fatigue...the fatigue. I'm so alone. Am I animal, vegetable, or mineral? Vegetable, I think. A close encounter with a memory, a girl with long red dread-locks, fast as a gazelle even on busy city streets walking with her arms swinging by her side, leaning forward like she was walking into the wind, wearing a bootleg

Raiders jacket...little thoughts bring little memories of her to me...I'm a young man from a small town with a very big imagination...a girl from my home town...

How necessary women are for us as foils, those little girls in bloom who knock on the door late at night, wearing white tonight, looking pure as a dove, wanting to slow tango to Thin Lizzy...preferably long legged cool innocent young women with discriminating hearts.

I'd rather starve than listen to the bourgeoisie.

I'd rather starve than listen to jazz.

I'd rather starve than talk to the bourgeoisie.

I'm imagining that I'm listening to *She's Like Heroin to Me* by The Gun Club. I'm walking down the street with my hands around her hips sharing the danger.

I'm clutching a sheet from a Sunday paper with some old stuff in it. Everything is old stuff, everything is dust. This old stuff is by D.H. Lawrence:

How beastly the bourgeois is.
Especially the male of the species—
Nicely groomed, like a mushroom,
Standing there so sleek and erect and eyeable—
And, like a fungus, living on the remains of a bygone life,
Sucking his life out of the dead leaves of greater life than his own.

It's the nighttime and I'm still the Nighttime Boy. Time to go down Deep Ellum where the whores with the fit pussy answer to the howl for doggy style.

Deep Ellum was the red light district in Dallas in the Twenties. They had a country blues song about it called *Deep Ellum Blues* or sometimes *Deep Elem Blues*.

Oh, sweet mama. Daddy got them Deep Ellum blues.

Then later it's the movie on the video player. I see the elegant setting with the beach house perspective where wifey is unhappy. The wife is the actress with the white skin, the dyed blonde hair, the fittest kind of Deep Ellum pussy. Her character in the movie is a good girl at heart who loves her Mom and her family. She's not cock mad but a pure blonde Catholic girl from modest circumstances who got married to a brute who thinks he owns her like he owns their home, the elegant Deco masterpiece looking out over the Big Sur-style beach house perspective.

There, in the movie on the video on the TV screen, the husband mounts her and fucks her up the ass with his stallion masculinity. When he's pumped everything into her and is satisfied he feels good. He pulls his actor cock out of her and heads for the shower, his declining cock slapping first against his left thigh and then against his right. In the shower he pisses. She lies on their mutual bed, still throbbing and shaking, hating him, planning a brave future.

The actress—not her character—must be like a whore. Down in Deep Ellum I'm just a kind of whore myself and I've loved other whores. I'm some kind of impudent nigger. Cars pass by with booming systems.

Jesse once told me that the bedroom is the intellectual gymnasium but I'm not so sure about that. I tend to think, Deep Ellum way, that the whole dirty subject has to be looked at coldly and without romance. Neither Jesse nor me go to Deep Ellum looking for love. There is little of love about our trips.

Then, when I just want to nod off or vomit or both, he phones in from the other side of town.

'Hi, Jesse,' I say. 'I'm the Nighttown boy again.'

'Hi,' he says, 'you still out of it?'

'Yep.' I laugh. 'And reading Barbara Pym. Novels by Barbara Pym really do me in.'

'I'm reading Bret Easton Ellis.' Jesse laughs. 'See you tomorrow, yeah?'

'Yeah, yeah, listen…it's the fatigue. I need to shut up. Bye.'

Time is on his side.

Sad man blues

Nigel avoids seeing us—generally speaking.

He gets Diazepam from his doctor, methadone from the Maudsley Clinic, heroin from the Barrier Block. He gets on the phone from time to time for plaintive, truculent, conversations, always trying to quit the band using 'I'm not worthy' arguments. These chats end with

Jesse shouting at him to fuck off, be sensible, and get with the programme.

Subliminal Kids keep rising up like an atomic bomb despite ourselves and Nigel—a veteran of being perched on the edge of success—no longer feels man enough for the gig; rehearsals, recording sessions, weekly gigs, occasional interviews, morons wanting to waste time making videos, wild groupies scratching at our front doors, things that make me stutter and roll my eyes, responsibilities. With dreams come responsibilities. It's so long since I've had money in my pocket that I'd forgotten what it's like.

It's happening for us but not for him.

We show up at a venue in the van. He comes late under his own steam, sets up his kit, does a brief sound-check, and disappears into the men's room for half an hour. He comes out, talks with us a while, and nods off in the dressing room.

Before the band goes on stage he wakes up, prettifies himself, and snaps to attention. He's never anything other than an extravagantly brilliant drummer, albeit one who sometimes looks like he's about to collapse on top of his kit. Young boys and girls in the crowd gather intimately around the stage, all milky, sexy, only pubic hair on their bodies. Preston averts his gaze though these are agreeable intelligent kids.

After the encores he goes right back into the men's

room to emerge much later, ask me for his money, and nod off in the van on the way back to Brixton.

I don't treat his frantic phoned-in resignations too seriously. We like him too much, vice versa, and we need him around. One of the reasons London's indifference is giving way to London fascination is because Preston— our metal guru no matter what—sits behind our drum kit. The lack of full-band rehearsals cramps Jesse's style—he needs to put new songs into the set on a regular basis but that's no longer practical.

Nigel is a *National Enquirer* kind of romantic guy. He keeps snakes. He owns a black swamp snake and two pythons. These are his only soul brothers. He wears classic rock musician black leather jackets with us and sometimes a silk jacket when hanging out with his wife.

Jesse is asleep in his room and I'm making coffee in the kitchen. I have this extraordinary woman called Jessica in my bedroom and she is sleeping tight. Out of the blue the front door explodes with unprofessional percussion, the clatter accompanied by Nigel screaming 'You two Irish cunts!! Get up and let me in! Let me in this minute!!' He sounds offensively superior and British. I stand perfectly still, perplexed. Everybody else is in bed. Complete silence is my best policy. But the fucker knows our hours, that it's unlikely we've gone out for the day: 'I know you're in there and if you don't open the door this second I'm going to kick it in. I want my kit. Give me back my kit this second!' He starts kicking the door, which we've reinforced with expensive Chubb locks and steel sheeting to withstand Pigs, London Electricity Board and other State enemies.

The pandemonium brings Jesse out of the bed and he joins me in the kitchen, naked and defenceless but for a half-erect cock. He raises his eyes to heaven. There is something new in Nigel's tone, and it's obvious to the two of us that he is really leaving the Kids this time.

'Fuck off Nigel. Go away. We're still in bed,' I lie, though this is unlikely to avoid an inevitable obnoxious incident.

'Leave me in you cunts!' His voice laden with spittle and frustration and alcohol and twenty-seven years too much.

'We're not gonna let you in, man, you're drunk,' shouts Jesse. 'Come back later when you're sober.'

Preston says nothing else but starts punching the door with his bare fists and kicking it methodically.

Jesse whispers to me: *He's going to break down that door eventually, it's going to break any minute. What'll we do?*

I suggest we trap him.: I'll retreat into the living room, drawing him in after me; Jesse'll hide in the bathroom and ambush him from behind. We'll restrain him and try to get him under control.

Round about then Jessica, no doubt intrigued by the

high drama, shows up in the hall dressed in her knickers and a blanket she has pulled around herself. None of this is making the right impression on her. I put a cup of black coffee I've poured for myself into her hand and shoo her back into bed.

The door gives way in slow motion. Wood cracks, nails give, hinges loosen, our front door opens. Preston is inside our home and he and me are staring at one another, embarrassment mixing with anger and confusion. I know he knows he's acting like a real cunt. I move backwards into the sitting room according to plan; he follows me in, lunging blindly. His poor valuable hands are a mass of raw meat from punching the door. The man is all kicked out, punched out, blood, sweat and spittle.

Not for the first or last time, me and Jesse do a pincer movement.

Jesse appears from nowhere, catches him from behind in a restraining hold. Nigel elbows Jesse in the balls, and lunges towards me again. I move to avoid him, he rushes past me, and I come in behind to catch him unfairly in a chokehold, cutting off his air supply. Pigs are banned from chokeholds—you can kill people doing this. Nigel moves up and down in involuntary spasms, trying to talk but incapable. Then I feel his body relax in my arms like he's just come.

Fainting, he slumps onto the ground, never out of my

grip, like I'm lowering him into a bath.

'You've killed him!' Jesse shouts, almost crying.

Jessica emerges from our bedroom fully dressed, looking at me weirdly, walking past me, going out the front door.

Preston is white as a sheet: I think I've killed him too.

Very slowly, like he's waking from a deep sleep, he comes back to us. We help him up from the ground and put him sitting on a couch. All three of us are in a daze, a certain fraternity returns for one last second; this is a situation we're in together. Nigel is unwell in so many ways—sore, dehumanised, drug-sick, sick from fainting, sex-sick. Fighting and fainting sobers him up some and he is sharp again.

'You still want your kit?' Jesse asks curtly.

'Yeah,' he says, furious that we attacked him back, that he lost the fight.

He gets up and walks out the door. We follow him out onto the landing, talking to his back. Jesse tells him to go over to LX's place where his drum kit is stored.

'Yeah, yeah,' Nigel says, elbowing me out of his way as he walks off, leaving a trail of blood behind him.

He gets into the lift and it takes him to the ground floor. He gets out, looks up at us, and marches over to LX's block. Jesse goes inside to phone LX to warn him that Preston is on his way. I suddenly notice the homies out on their balconies all around me, aroused by the shouting and the fighting. Seeing Nigel leave our place all blood splattered, they misinterpret things, assume we've kicked the shit out of him. Shouts of nigger approval, respectful looks, high fives, other types of thumbs-up coming my way.

All the blood comes from his fists.

That afternoon we were heading into the tube station when Jesse put an arm across my chest and stopped me in my tracks. Going through the ticket barrier up ahead of us was Nigel, stumbling around, clutching some of his biggest cymbals—with and without their flight cases—in his hands. LX had told us he'd taken his cymbals. We let him go on ahead and, an hour later, went to the Record and Tape Exchange in Notting Hill. There was blood on the doorknobs going into the shop so we knew we were in the right place. Inside there was blood on the steps leading upstairs and blood on his cymbals on sale there.

Jesse rang Noko and told her to come down and buy the stuff. He reckoned Nigel would eventually resurface with his tail between his legs and would need his equipment back.

That was our final meeting.

The rules have changed nigger

I tuned in to this black pirate station late one night when they announced, strangely and wonderfully, that LL was in the studio waiting to take calls from his fans.

For an hour the man stayed on the air, a good humoured shimmering black voice taking questions about his words, his women, his music. He sounded very real to me. Pink cookies in a plastic bag getting crushed by buildings. Genet said that the extravagant adventure of white America is doubtless exhausted and that it will dissolve and fade, revealing at last what is cheerfully devouring it; the black nation which was caught within it, itself traversed by liberating currents, liberating movements, producing long screams of misery and joy.

In Hollywood during the LA riots skateboarding looters stole crotchless panties from upmarket department stores and Madonna's bustier from warehousing down in MacArthur Park, the Spanish Harlem of LA. Other looters concentrated on stuff like cockroach spray and diapers. One man was found with a packet of sunflower seeds and two cartons of milk. He was held on $15,000 bail.

'The black man is an intelligence test the white man is taking,' said the Rev Albert Cleage, a Detroit civil rights leader in the Sixties.

After the LA disturbances one gang leader, Dandy,

recalled: 'Our car was pulled over. When we asked what we'd done wrong, a big redneck cop said *The rules have changed Nigger!* and hit me in the face with his pistol.'

Satan in the architecture

The dedicated criminal knows when it's time to quit, when there's no long-term future in the criminal lifestyle. If he's a real desperado/hooligan he will burn the candle at both ends until the final moment and, when all that can be gained has been gained, perform a disappearing trick, get out ahead and evaporate. The authentic criminal—the cold motherfucker—knows that to get out safely and get out of the frame he has to put somebody else into it. You've got to find a patsy, have a victim. You've got to find a non-innocent party and let him carry the can for you.

In any case we'd always rhetorically been committed to a philosophy of constant change and had been in Brixton too long. Lambeth Council were determined to see the back of us and money didn't roll in like it once had. The council were on to us, somebody'd squealed us up, and they were aware that a professional squatting cabal was working in their midst—they had investigators on our trail. Each and every one of our squats was recovered from us, usually by a lethal weapon called a

PIO—a legal loophole meaning *Person Intending Occupancy*. All they had to do was offer a given squat to a homeless family; when the lease was signed, Lambeth would show up at the front door and give us two day's notice. Most of these PIOs were fake, and our emptied squats joined their stock of unoccupied housing.

Even the Volvo, emblematic of our entire lifestyle, eventually gave out and LX began to fray at the edges. We bought him a new car but things were not the same.

As our factory phonelines got disconnected one by one, the various creditors owed money by Jah Screw and Lisa finally got court orders to enter the premises and seize goods there. The leased t-shirt equipment assholes, Telecom, Lambeth Council, yabba, yabba, yabba: these and other enemies of promise wanted their money or Screw's goods. They were not to know than Screw had flown the coop years back, and that all that remained was an empty shell: an office without office equipment and a factory painted black for illegal rave purposes.

There were six different legal situations concerning sums of more than two thousand pounds. Lambeth were owed over five thousand in back rent and were more serious about demanding instant payment than the others. Eventually a letter came from the courts saying that Lambeth could regain possession of their property four weeks after the date on the letter. So we emptied the factory, selling nearly everything we could transport to the Record and Tape Exchange, giving away desks, tables and filing cabinets to Rodrigo Gomez, whose punk promotions were now techno promotions.

Four Saturdays in a row before the eviction we threw raves; Jay and his pals supplying the Es and the crack, Rodrigo selling the tickets on his mobile phone, a deal being done on the take from the drug sales. No doubt Jay didn't keep his side of the deal, but that's showbiz. In the days leading up to the eviction we all went down there and rang everybody we could think of.

'End of an era, motherfucker,' Jesse said to me the last night. 'Anyway, time we moved on and up.'

I was sentimental but it was midnight in our perfect world.

At the same time, we got evicted from Ralston House and decided to move to legitimate accommodation in North London. We put all our stuff into cardboard boxes, moved into our one remaining squat, unpacked nothing, went flat hunting for the first time. This period lasted five weeks. During that time I heard no music, but I watched lots of green and white television in the afternoons with the curtains closed. LX came over less often, we were no longer living across from one another. I sometimes went to his place to use our last remaining phoneline. The weather was picking up after a cold lean winter. In those weird days I'd sit out on his balcony talking internationally on the phone, watching the heterotrash down below on the ground, listening to tapes LX had made from my own album collection.

Youth of Seattle demand sex

I've got a new girlfriend called Alwyn Falkow.

Alwyn is a linguini-thin kid, limbs delicate as an eyelid, cold as ice cream and just as sweet. She has studs through both nipples and one through her left eyebrow. She has spiked mousey-blonde hair and trusting dark brown eyes. She is 13 and comes from Seattle, where all the bands come from. She wears a t-shirt which says: 'I hate you and I hate your Jesus.'

Alwyn is part of the Seattle Youth Decadence Campaign, and she gave me their leaflet *Youth of Seattle Demand Sex:*

"Much of the neurosis of today's youth is caused by anxiety due to the lack of a decent sex life. Wilhelm Reich recommended that the state provide free hotels for youth to have sex in, to relieve anxiety caused because kids have to have sex in alleys. In addition to Reich's suggestion, The Youth Decadence Campaign demands that the city provides Seattle's youth with free prostitutes. Youth that are seen as being physically attractive and 'popular' by capitalist society's false value system, hold an unfair monopoly of sex partners. Lack of sex in the early young adult years can lead to an inferiority complex that may never heal, even leading to suicide. Thus, we demand free and decent sex for all youth, regardless of race, gender, class or physical attractiveness."

I be here—then I disappear

Billy The Kid: How does it feel?
Pat Garrett: It feels like times are changing.

I first met Jesse at an arty party in the Dublin Resource Centre around 1984. I noticed him lurking around multiband hardcore gigs, and then somebody told me he played bass with a rockabilly band called Grown Up Country Boys. I never spoke with him until that night in the Resource Centre.

The DRC was a cheap vegetarian restaurant in the Temple Bar area, with a left-wing bookshop out front and progressive printers upstairs. On weekend nights they rented it out for parties exploring the sex/art underground. The party I met Jesse at was organised by a mutual pal, a boy called Ricky O'Neill whose folks were rich architects. Ricky looked like the young Mia Farrow—only more so. At Ricky's party the music was by The Golden Shower, Ramones soundalikes led by a tall loner called Paul Swick. Swick had a sad girlfriend called Ramona Thunders, and he bought his pulses and grains every Saturday at the Temple Bar Wholefood Co-Operative.

The Shower played in an unsafe crumbling basement—I thought the ceiling was going to cave in from the weight of the crowd upstairs. While The Shower were racing through a dehydrated adrenaline-driven version of The Beach Boys' *Oh, Caroline No* I spotted Jesse standing at the other side of the stage, staring coldly at a tuneless but charismatic Paul Swick.

Upstairs an indie filmmaker calling himself Northern Protestant showed his Super 8 movie of naked women kickboxing. Protestant lived in Jesse's house so when a gang of lesbians kicked over his projector and punched Protestant, Jesse came over and asked me to intervene. The street politics of the lesbians was wicked—and I enjoyed Protestant's prank. I was on the horns of a dilemma which I solved by quitting the party with Ricky O'Neill. But I took note of Jesse's cold charisma. The following afternoon, when I ran into him in Bewleys Cafe, we got to talking.

In fact we ranted at one another for an hour about what a bad band The Golden Shower were. We came to the conclusion that The Shower's idea about music was all right—just that they were all wrong. Out of that jest we decided that Jesse should quit rockabilly. He wanted

Grown Up Country Boys to go in the demented direction of The Gun Club but the lead singer—a North Dublin pretty boy in the Eddie Cochran mould—entertained commercial fantasies.

A week later a former discus champion adonis called Pete approached us out of the Temple Bar fog to say he'd heard we were thinking of putting a band together, that he was a guitarist, wanted to come in on it. He looked great in his ankle-length brown leather coat. Jesse and Pete formed Subliminal Kids in Temple Bar—then the band rehearsal part of town—with Pete on guitar and me on the phone. The first drummer didn't work out: he couldn't pronounce 'subliminal'. Within the month it emerged that Pete didn't play guitar as good as he looked. But style was everything when Subliminal Kids crawled out of the Temple Bar slime of painters, moviemakers and underground music.

Pete, replaced after eight weeks by Powell, eventually got a good bit part in The Commitments and, on the back of that, went to America. I see him from time to time in American TV courtroom dramas, where he usually plays sex killers or rapists.

We worked for years and years on that band—sailors out of sight of land—and sometimes it looked like we'd never get everywhere. Then, when things were going their worst, things started going right and we saw land.

The problem was our agenda. We felt we could

purvey that mythical beast—serious rock music—so we had no place in the whore-infested waters of the London music scene. A famous Irish guitarist once told Jesse that more people disappeared without a trace between Old Compton Street, Berwick Street and Charing Cross Road than ever disappeared into the Bermuda Triangle.

Jesse was good looking enough and talented enough as a singer and songwriter to have made it much earlier in his life—but he had Super 8 ideals and Cinemascope aspirations. It took him a long time to launch his agenda onto the planet and took its toll on our friendship.

I was supposed to be the manager but it's the manager's job to make money and, in music, you don't make money if you don't compromise. Jesse didn't want to compromise and I was just as bad. In the early Nineties there was a break in the clouds: ritualised rock'n'roll, with lyrics, economical guitar solos and all the bodily trimmings, was briefly in fashion. Don't ask me why.

Miguel Gomez played a big part in the Kids' rise. The first promoter to give us a gig in London, he booked bands into The Boston Arms, an old Irish pub in Tufnell Park. He put the Kids on in the middle of a three band bill, a little beneath our dignity, but we were happy to get the feel of London before headlining. As it happened there were about a hundred and fifty people at the gig and a hundred of them were there for the Kids. The

Dublin alternative scene had moved lock, stock and barrel to London—busy buying Super 8 cameras at the Record and Tape Exchange—and most of them showed up in Tufnell Park.

Gomez came from California, his family were Mexican. When I first met him his despised father was a visiting Professor of Psychology at Cambridge. Gomez was about thirty but looked a lot younger. He was tall, with dark gypsy eyes and curly black hair. The night of that first gig Jesse said: 'Miguel there is a bit of a trousers filler, isn't he?'

He always had a teenage girl in tow. The girls stayed young, and Gomez never really grew old. The first few years in London I didn't have that much to do with him, but he worked on his gig, sussing out new venues, discovering bands that later got deals, squatting North London houses where he'd hole up with fresh nubiles.

When Subliminal Kids finally came to terms with London, and when Nigel pulled the spotlight onto us, Gomez was the expert we needed in our team. He knew the cool venues to play, the support bands who'd draw a big crowd of their own, the journalists who'd give us publicity. While Gomez managed London for us, me and Jesse finally pulled up our trousers and went to work. I got on the phone, typed up new biogs, got us a two album deal with a big indie that never paid royalties and found us an agent who actually did some work. Jesse for his part created new music, got a new haircut, applied urban sensibilities to his songs. We lost some fans but we gained a following.

Suddenly that which was private went national. We came to terms with the fact that we'd never be the Rolling Stones—change the world—but we were soon drawing eight hundred people a gig.

Word reached us from Ireland that The Golden Shower had broken up, Paul Swick marrying a bitch from the U2 office. Over in London Subliminal Kids won; there was nothing left to prove. Which meant we didn't have to lean on one another any more. When we started working on the Kids Jesse was a boy and I was a young man. The band swallowed up a part of our lives.

Jesse hated London during the Thatcher years but, oddly enough, when they were over it wasn't any fun to be there—he had nothing to hate any more. We Irish were stronger than the English. We squatters had lost our squats but we'd won the argument. By driving us overground they forced some of the best and the brightest to enter their mainstream. Being the vicious amoeba-like guerrillas that they were, squatters survived while the Yuppies went to the wall.

In the early Nineties I, socio-youthful, rioted in Hyde Park with my generation and we struck terror into the hearts of our enemies. Maybe that's just bourgeois praise for bourgeois achievements...

And we'd spent so many days and nights living together in the repressed world of the marginalised, talking over everything, never owning a video player, a camcorder or sports gear, that we needed space. Paddy left town. My arse was looking for better weather. The best friends must part.

Jesse lives in Madrid. I live in Berlin. I also have a small apartment in Algeciras.

In Dublin they've stopped dropping notes through one another's flatland letterboxes. Now it's all e-mails to séamus.shoneen@gobshite.com.

Temple Bar is just a tourist attraction now; the attraction is that it was once the bohemian part of town. The bohemians are older—some are mathematicians, some are carpenter's wives. Ricky O'Neill don't look like Mia Farrow any more, but he produces arthouse movies. Northern Protestant has reverted to his real name and his real background—now he is a Northern Protestant. The site of the Dublin Resource Centre houses the chic Arthouse where artfags collect grants and subventions. The miserable, demented, starving ghosts of those long-ago Super 8 artists come out at night, when the tourists go home.

We were each other's heroes, just for one day. I manage his band; it's boring now but it was boring then too. We just had each other, drugs and the nighttime.

It's not dark out yet, but it's getting there.

Meet her at the Love Parade. I want to dance. I want to get down tonight.

Surf's up. The tide is high and I'm moving on. The sun is out, and I want some.

Kim: One time Mick Jagger was backstage at a Lou Reed gig trying to be nice. Reed gets three encores so he storms offstage. Jagger says to him, 'Great gig, Lou.' Reed just keeps on walking so Jagger walks along behind him, still trying to be nice. 'Have you played here before, Lou?' Jagger says by way of small talk. 'How the fuck would I know?' barks Loopy Lou as he disappears into his dressing room.

Jesse: On the new album he has Fred Maher, Maureen Tucker, good people—it's real good—but there's all this ridiculous corporate shit on the sleeve notes about 'Graphics'. It says that NEW YORK is one of the first CDs to display graphics on TV sets. It says the listener can now see Lou Reed's lyrics on the TV while listening to his music! That you can see the lyrics in English, Spanish, French. Pompous asshole! It fucking says that CD GRAPHICS equipment can be bought from the Fall of '89 on!

Kim: Yeah, well, he learned a few things about making money from Warhol. Reed has this thing about having studied poetry with Delmore Schwartz, some fucking minor American poet. Lou ain't exactly a song and dance man. Some of those rock founding fathers are becoming totally pompous...self-congratulatory.

Jesse: Once they wanted blowjobs. Now they want respect. I don't ever want respect.

Kim: No, you're still at the blowjobs stage, my friend.

Jesse: And why not?

Kim: Why not indeed.

Carry go bring come

August '98. I fly into London on my way to Reading Festival, pick up my access all areas pass at the Holiday Inn. Cut to ordinary men and women going about their ordinary tasks, observed from the distance by us people of the White Subway. Rancid, Prodigy, Lee Scratch Perry, and the Beasties playing for the sun. Mosh in the massacre at Rancid. I move with a Frisco Kid when Rancid cover *If The Kids Are United*. And the Frisco Kid never returns. Not dumb enough. Dust on my tongue.

The Beasties are limp by comparison—something is not quite right or connecting. Wealth and age cause them contradictions so I leave twenty minutes into their set. Nothing surprises me now. Nothing frightens me now. Music still moves me. Some Islamics say people shouldn't listen to music because it stirs the soul and only God should stir the soul. Music is the diabolic. The Beastie Boys must grow old/inelegant like the Stones grew old and inelegant if they want to stir our souls again. They can be a cartoon or become an old black and white photograph. Now that Beck is El Pussy Cat, can you still dance at their revolution?

And who owns Death TV?

Boys from the county hell

God's finger touched him, and he slept.
  Lord Tennyson.
Search and you'll find...sanctuary.
  The Cult

LX comes up to our place at 7.30AM.

For the first time in years we're awake in the morning and dressed, albeit hyped up and wobbly. Showering. Shaving. Listening to Thin Lizzy and Joe Tex. For five weeks we've been, for all intents and purposes, homeless. We're in our last squat—which is desolate and unhomely. The plumbing is fucked and home smells dirty because poor people lived here before us; nothing maintained, nothing painted for years, such furniture as is left behind fit for the scrap heap. I'm surrounded by the heterotrash who hate us, see us for social perverts.

We have lots of money under our mattresses, play our cards close to our chest. Last Thursday I handed over cash money to get a North London flat from Naomi Solomon, a crazy Israeli lady in her sixties who has fallen for my Irish charms. Jesse plans to move in with an ex-girlfriend for a while, with a view to moving to Brighton in the winter. It's time to say goodbye for eternity to Brixton and to Nigel.

'I need money for the van,' mumbles LX, on his way to score a hirevan for the day. Jesse gives him the cash and a dodgy-but-clean driving license we've picked up. LX looks miserable and sullen disappearing out into the morning city, sustained by a few joints and some vicious coffee.

The plan is typically two-sided and perverse. In the morning we go to Nigel's funeral in the van. When we've planted him we'll return to Brixton, pack our cardboard boxes into the van, and LX will drive us to North London, where half of a Victorian terraced house, all decked out with carpets, suites of furniture, dishwashers, yabba, yabba, yabba, awaits me. I'm to store Jesse's stuff until he gets a home of his own. His ex-bitch wants him around but not his detritus. In the evening LX will return the van to the van-hire crowd and go home to his squat on the estate. All alone and lonesome. He smells lonely.

In Zen theory I'm amused by the idea of going to the

funeral—everything about Nigel has a comic side to it—
but the middle class Irish boy buried deep down inside
me is horrified. Nigel is out there in soul limbo holding
a sawn off shotgun to my head. The gunblast goes off
every five minutes, and my skull rips apart in slo-mo
psychedelics every day.

Four days ago we came home from a party to find a
message from Nigel's father on the answering machine:
'Hello, Jesse…and Kim. Could you give me a call please?
There is something I must tell you.'

I said it sounded like Nigel was in trouble again. Jesse
said: 'No. It sounds bad. It sounds real bad.' I said:
'Nah! The stupid fucker has been busted or something.'
Jesse said: 'No. I don't think so. The old man sounds
really bad.' He was afraid to make the return call and, of
course, the news was as bad as possible.

Nigel and Jimmy met up as arranged at Brixton tube
station.

Jimmy was Nigel's oldest buddy, crony, confidante,
conspirator from earliest schooldays. I'd met him on and
off since we'd first hung out with Nigel. He was a shifty
somewhat androgynous layabout, a part-time junkie
who was economical with the facts. We didn't find out

about his adventure with Nigel until five months later when Jesse ran into him on the tube and he, very reluctantly, spilled the beans. In fact he got off the tube before Jesse got the whole story out of him and I don't think I've seen him since. He may well be dead. So I only have a sketchy idea of what happened in the Barrier Block.

Jimmy was flush with funds. He too had a Japanese wife (Do some Jap women like weak addicted men who can be controlled?) and she was generous with her cash. They'd arranged to meet at Brixton tube station in the late afternoon. The notion was that Jimmy would hand over the money to Nigel, the streetwise one, and Nigel would go get the junk. Jimmy and Nigel walked down behind Brixton Market, two old comrades in all of their adventures, heading towards the entrance to the Barrier Block. Nigel'd lived with junkies in the Barrier Block after The Cult. He used to put on a balaclava and, wielding a billyclub, smash in the doors of other junkie's squats, kick the junkies to the ground, beat their heads in until they told him where their stash was, steal their stash and whatever cash was lying around. It was ironic that he should press his eject button in the same place. Jimmy waited in the forecourt and Nigel disappeared inside.

Nigel disappeared forever.

'You just hang on out here, you worthless faggot,' Nigel shouted as he marched confidently towards the entrance of the Block, 'and I'll deal with these cunts and come back with something nice for ya.' He waved as he shut the door behind him.

He went in there a laughing sentient white boy. The next people who saw him were Barrier Block heroin dealers and they didn't give a shit if he lived or died. So he died! He'd assured Jimmy he'd come right back with the stuff but, being Nigel, he had to try the product first. Later, via his parents, who heard it via the Pigs, I heard that he was dead ages when they found him. Jimmy hung around in front of the Block for almost an hour (which was brave of him given the neighbourhood but he was looking forward to his fix so he had conflicting priorities) before storming off cursing Nigel. It's a big big building and he had no way of knowing exactly where Nigel was lost inside of it. Nigel was always secretive about exactly where his dealers lived. LX said that, when he chauffeured Nigel down there, he'd been ordered to wait in the Volvo. When the Pigs showed up it was too late. I think somebody made an anonymous phonecall after they carried a dead Nigel out into a corridor and, presumably, dragged him a discreet distance away from where they actually lived. That didn't matter a fuck, he was DOA. His folks didn't really want to work out the details.

The following morning at dawn three Pigs called to Nigel's home and woke his father up. It can't have been big news to the Pigs, another junkie dead of an overdose in Brixton, but at least he was white so they had to contact his family. Apparently they were nice enough about it.

At the end of the game we had one, almost sexual, bit of information about Nigel that he never had about himself—we knew the nature of his dying. The mystery was that such a seasoned druggie could have mistaken his dosage. The suspicion must always be that he let it happen.

I always thought of him as a post-modern rock star. All his bands—Sex Gang Children, Theatre of Hate, The Cult—were third generation imitations of inspired music made when Nigel, Jesse, LX and me were kids. Nigel had a spirit of life inside him that went back to the roots. He was one of those desperate old bluesmen who'd gone to the cross-roads to sell his soul to the Devil so often that the Devil had lost interest. The Devil was just laughing at him. Nigel saw the tragedy, the beauty, the comedy. If he'd known any other artists he'd have been one.

LX pulled it off again; the dodgy license convinced the van hire bastards.

'You know, LX,' Jesse quipped, looking manly in the black Comme Des Garçons suit Noko'd bought him in a fit of demented fanmania. 'We've opened up yet another window of opportunity for you with that driving license.

Now that you've gotten the van…how much of a deposit did you have to give them?'

'A hundred,' answered LX, exhausted, strung out, but brought to attention by the mention of an anti-career opportunity.

'Now you've got that nice shiny van outside and they've gotten a ton off you for it and they don't know the fuck who you are or where it is…do I have to draw a map?'

'No. No,' LX said, speaking very softly, cheering up slightly. And then he was the first of us to come back down to earth; not his usual role. 'Perhaps we should get going.'

We piled inside our hirevan and headed across South London to Greenwich where the church service and burial were to be. I got caught up in my own irrelevant daydream as he drove us through semi-imaginary South London suburbs while housewives milled around doing their hypershopping, adolescent girls and boys played out courtship rituals, black women looked for cheap things, and commuters commuted—a chirpy morning full of sunshine and spirit.

LX turned on the radio and it brought me back to earth. They were playing some shitty optimistic California stuff, Fleetwood Mac or The Eagles. Don't let the sound of your own wheels drive you crazy. Very appropriate. The news came on. In our funeral frenzy we'd almost forgotten that the Tories under John Major had won yet another election the day before.

This was the first time I'd been to the funeral of a style statement in black leather and denim. No doubt Nigel was *actually* coffined in either his best suit—the one Kaz bought him so she could bring him to the MTV annual Christmas party, the one he wore the night he came backstage at The Marquee—or in an undertaker's shroud, which he'd probably have enjoyed. Onstage.

The family church came right out of an English Victorian whodunnit, evocative of the village green, cricket, maiden aunts, whist drives. We parked our van off behind the church, alighted, slowly approached the 19th Century dream machine perched oh-so-scenically on a grassy mossy hill while the debris of the modern world milled all around—motorways, minicabs, telephone booths, video stores, lowlifes, the outer suburbs of sexual possibility. Inside the grounds of the church there were lots of suburban types—Nigel's family connections—in their funeral wear. 'Oh, fuck!' one of us said. I don't know which one, but we all felt the same. Now we had arrived to assist in the burying of Nigel.

Handsome looking young men, much younger than Nigel, stood near the gates, all embarrassed and uncomfortable. Some of them, especially the ones with the smooth, almost hairless faces, had obviously never been to a funeral before. Telltale earrings and flashy haircuts indicated that they were fans of some aspect of Nigel's Goth-infested life. But even these guys, the guys we might have had something in common with, were dressed up in their best Sunday clothes—the suits and jackets they kept for funerals, family occasions, girlfriends' staff parties. It is the way of the English to have such clothes in reserve. I never understood the English, though I liked some of them.

We headed into the church and found seats off to the side in the darkness and obscurity—where we'd always been more comfortable.

There were all sorts of people in that church but none of them, other than us, looked as if they'd ever been in a rock band. No members of The Cult, no Jeffrey Lee, not even Andi Sexgang. Classical music erupted from somewhere and we were called to attention.

The Protestant Minister had obviously known our Nigel. He talked about the schoolboy who played rugby but who wanted to do nothing else with his life other than drum. About him saving up for his first drum kit. About his first bands, local garage bands, his later successes and Top of the Pops appearances:

'Eventually Nigel left The Death Cult and formed with others, The Cult, who went on to huge international success. At the time of his death he was, as they say, *on the comeback trail* with his new band, Subliminal Kids...I suppose the one consolation we can take today is from the good news that John Major has been re-elected Prime Minister.'

It was funny to hear this weird Tory forced to talk of Death Cults and Subliminal Kids. Such is the linguistic power of rock'n'roll. Such is the danger of rock'n'roll. Nigel did his job.

Preacher Man said nothing about the specific nature of Nigel's death. Dying of an OD in the Barrier Block was not the kind of thing you could discuss at a social occasion. I could sense Preston's troubled spirit lingering in the air. He was free of Babylon's trouble, free at last, free from the world and all its trials. And that was just stoned middlebrow bullshit. Next thing I heard a car pass by with a booming system blasting out KRS One. I smiled for a second. Very Nigel, very city. A primitive, he'd feared dance music, knowing it was the enemy of every tradition he'd lived for as a musician. Just then the preacher began to wind down his awful service, giving details of where the interment would take place and what was the easiest route to take to get there.

The procession began. His brothers, big strong rugby players who looked like him only not so degenerate, carried the coffin. As they passed us by the tannoy system crackled into life and I heard some drumming; Nigel drumming *She Sells Sanctuary* by The Cult. It boomed out through that church, and for one vile moment we all heard him drumming for what he was worth in his prime when everything good was already behind him and everything bad lay ahead. Those drumming hands were up there in a box. He existed, behind the kit, in a lonely place where he faced down his demons through the beat. Nigel hated that record, it played a profound part in his destruction.

Every time I hear it on the radio—I hear it on the fucking radio all over the world—I think of that moment in that church.

We got lost, naturally enough, on the way to the graveyard. Jesse said: 'LX, you'd get lost on the way to your own funeral.' When we finally found the cemetery there were three funerals in action. I saw his parents by a grave and we rushed over there. His coffin was already in the ground and members of the family were throwing handfuls of dirt on top of the coffin. LX and Jesse went to join them. When they came back LX encouraged me to do the same but I was already freaked out enough by the sound of the clay hitting the wood, that awful hollow sound. I couldn't stand, either, to walk over to the edge of the grave and stare down.

I stayed a distance away and, when the service was over, walked towards the van saying to myself, *So this is how and where it'll end. See you later in a far country,* while LX and Jesse commiserated with the family.

To leave was to admit that there would be no bail for our boy this time. We left him there in that field untypical of him, another corpse in a South London field full of corpses.

Down in the ground where the deadmen go.

Down in the ground where the deadmen go.

We got back into our van, LX drove us back to Brixton. That was the end of that. We left it all behind, burying more than our man in that South London graveyard. We had already packed our bags, prepared to seek out new territories. We were the boys from the County Hell, Paddy Public Enemy, too cute for failure, too young for defeat, too young for peace and quiet, looking for pussy, looking for meaning. We would not go down easily or die young, our investment in our beliefs was one too many mornings for us to throw it all away. I've never been back to Brixton or to Nigel's grave.

It was a serious time.

Writer and musician Joe Ambrose lived in Brixton, working as a band manager, in the late Eighties and early Nineties. A member of Islamic Diggers, Ambrose has performed on stage with John Cale and Lydia Lunch. He co-wrote a biography of William Burroughs, *Man from Nowhere*. He also co-produced the Islamic Diggers CD '10%--file under Burroughs' which features Burroughs, the Master Musicians of Joujouka, Marianne Faithfull, Bomb The Bass, and Paul Bowles. His writing has appeared in anthologies published by Pulp Faction, Serpent's Tail and Codex. This is his first novel.